Diary of Ali's Prison Shop

by

Maria Sheikh

New Generation Publishing

- Prologue -

My childhood took place sometime between the decade of free love and the era of the Iron Lady, and you could say that my family life was as typical as one could expect in a society shaped by economical swings and an influx of migration.

I was always the first one to get my elder sister's already second-hand clothes, an experience that brought me to realise that jeans are not, nor have ever been, designed to last more than two siblings. I have a brother too, but he was fortunate enough to be omitted from the annual hand-me-down ritual. Just. Dad had briefly thought that a tailored trouser could look like a rather convincing set of plus-fours. If it hadn't been for the darsee charging too much (too much being any figure of legal tender) Aftab would have been walking down Oxford Road in the finest polyester.

Dad thought himself a savvy entrepreneur, although it should be noted that during any period of longstanding financial malaise words like 'entrepreneur' acquire a much looser definition. In other words, his entrepreneurial skill equated to being able to make five pounds last the entire week. I believe nowadays this would be more widely termed as being a skinflint, but as far as my dad was concerned he was the forerunner of the archetypal yuppie (despite being neither young nor professional, although urban just about passes as we lived in Manchester).

As I try to etch out our family portrait in my mind, the silhouette of a tank takes centre place. In place of a turret, Dad would wave a danda – a long, slender wooden stick – and instead of bullets he would scatter blunted words thick and fast, bringing down anyone and anything in his path or trying to escape from it. That said, it's worth bearing in mind that beneath the robust armour plating of tanks there is usually little more than an average-sized, fleshy, vulnerable human, no more resilient than an ant caught in a spider's web. You could say that my father was the type of man who could feel the weight of his own shadow, wishing he was capable of measuring up to it.

Then there was Mum. While my father lamented the burden of sunrays across his back, my mother would always have her face turned towards the warmth. She had this way of drifting momentarily out of the humdrum of daily routine and noticing the minor beauties that punctuate our lives: a cup of well brewed tea, a day without rain, and the powder-puff pink traces of bonbon candies along the contours of her fingertips. The corners of her lips would prick into a smile as tears chased themselves along her plump cheeks, all the while listening to her favourite songs crackle forth from the television. Thinking back on those years of watching dramas and films, cushioned between Mum and my siblings on our sunken couch and only vaguely comprehending a word of Urdu or Punjabi here and there, I recall telling her half a dozen times that it was merely a song and that the singing actress, whose voice would skip from high note to even higher note, wasn't really destined to be banished from her family's house for all eternity. For all my explanations, the tears did not cease; I have since learnt that this is the case with all my mother's tears.

My mother's existence was defined by a particular ritual: each morning she would pursue a silver whistle to her mouth, which would let out the ear-splitting declaration that morning had arrived and we had to get up. She would then begin the never-ending cycle of cleaning and cooking, taking the occasional hiatus to tend to the plump roses, daffodils and tulips that dotted our back yard; at the far back her pride and joy stretched tall in an enormous green tub – a miniature apple tree. The rule – the particularly bizarre rule – was that none of us besides her were allowed to reap the fruits of the tree, lest we bruise the fruit or, worse still, bruise the tree itself. To this day, I peel apple skins with delicate hesitation.

Each day, with only the exception of Sunday, Mum would perch upon the last step of the narrow staircase, awaiting the arrival of the post, praying with loosely clasped hands that a letter would arrive from her family in Pakistan. Sometimes I would echo her pose from the top step, studying her small frame. It was one of the rare moments of lull in our four-bedroom council-owned household, the place we had called home for some ten years.

Life shuffled along with foxtrot pacing, with my days oscillating back and forth between college and the mundane tropes of home-life: cooking, making chai tea, cleaning, siblings suffering sherbet-induced hyperactivity, Bollywood dramas featuring the classic storylines of love and loss, and making yet more chai tea, served with puff-pastry snaps and rusk biscuits – the only acceptable way of serving tea in an Asian household.

It is strange – outright peculiar, even – how you can don one identity when at home, but the moment

3

you step out the front door you acquire a different skin. It is inevitable, really, that the boundaries of those identities start to blur, that they begin to mingle in much the same way different languages can find themselves interwoven in the same conversation – and somehow meaning and clarity is never lost. I was never confused about my identity, although I will admit that if you were to ask me now what it means to be British and Asian I probably wouldn't be able to muster an answer – at least not one that chimes as being witty and enlightened. What I mean to say is: when I was growing up, I just accepted what was simply was.

We ate beans on toast with HP tomato sauce on Thursday nights, and on Fridays we ate keema on toast with HP brown sauce. We watched *Coronation Street* in the evenings and I had a picture of a young Ken Barlow pinned on my bedroom wall, and alongside him was a signed photograph of a dashing Amitabh Bachchan my mum had found at the market. It broke my heart some years later when I discovered that the scrawl with an inky marker-pen was the result of the market-seller's sense of artistic license. I didn't question how it could be that every person to visit our house bearing the same complexion as me could be either my uncle or my auntie (but strictly never aunt), nor did I exhaust myself wondering why I would adorn the back covers of my schoolbooks with sketches of my dream wedding dress – eroding a white crayon until it became nothing more than a blunt stub – yet alongside these drawings would be the fine flicks and undulating furls of henna patterns.

I don't mean to suggest that I never pondered a

moment or two over the oddities of my life's rhythm, shifting from bhangra to the Bee Gees and back again. Of course, there were times when I had to ask myself why the names of my siblings and I seemed pretty unorthodox compared to those of my school peers. I didn't know any other Malika, Miriam, Ferzana, or Aftab in my school. There came a point when I had seen my name misspelt far too many times and decided to adopt a moniker that I wouldn't have to spell out so often: Maria. It was no resounding gesture of political conformity; I was just sick of seeing Malika written all over my report cards. But then there were our neighbours, Mr and Mrs McCarthy, who were an altogether more complicated affair; they would talk in terms of 'us' and 'them', and seemed to enjoy regurgitating the same remarks about the country heaping up a funeral pyre and something or another about the river Tiber foaming with blood. I had asked my geography teacher where exactly the Tiber was and was told it was a river in Italy that runs through Rome. As a result, I put the McCarthy's ceaseless jabbering about the bloody river down to a bad holiday experience, although that always struck me as somewhat dubious in light of how much they would harp on about 'foreigners'. If they could not bear a weekend caravan trip in Rhyl because of the 'daft accent', I couldn't much imagine them in Rome…

Mrs McCarthy would reassure us from across the fence that 'we were alright' – usually when Dad was waltzing up and down the garden path with his danda in hand, waving it at the other neighbour's cat, who had deemed our flowerbeds to be its litter-tray. For a long time, I had assumed that the omitted conclusion of this remark was: 'we were alright as neighbours'; it wasn't until one day Aftab's football found itself in the McCarthy's pond, sending their one goldfish surfing towards certain death into a bed of chrysanthemums, did I realise what she had actually meant.

'Take your damn ball out of here ya lil' paki!' From my bedroom window, I watched the argument ensue, with Dad waving his arms in the air whilst Mr McCarthy gesticulated back and forth from the pond to my father and Aftab, his finger poised as if it alone could eject us from the country.

Each time he demanded that we return to where we'd come from he'd jab his finger in yet another direction; in that moment, my feet seemed to somehow sink deeper into the floorboards, as if I'd become fastened into the structure of that house. This was where I'd come from, this was the place I called home. I didn't even know where Pakistan lay on the map.

This was January 1972 and this was my life. College girl, second-eldest daughter, Malika, Maria, Asian, British, lover of flares and golden bangles, pioneer of Mancunian Punjabi, aspiring poet and maker of misshapen roti. My life and my priorities were due for a shake-up though, and as my mother would say: your kismet is your kismet – your fate is your own doing.

The Shop - Where it all started

"So, what you're saying is, more or less, that you have, in a matter of speaking, bought a shop?" My dad and I stared at each other, his heavy brow and dumpy, mottled eyelids hanging low over his brown eyes, like poorly upholstered jabots that had seen better days. "I mean, that is, at the end of the day, what you are pretty much saying, right?" I added to my earlier comment, which seemed to have drifted so far past my father's head it was already halfway down the M6 and swiftly approaching Birmingham.

"You know, beti, you don't half-life like to take a lot of detours when trying to say the simplest thing. It's not a very attractive quality. No man will want a wife who has nothing to say," my father responded, to which my mother glanced up briefly from the socks she'd been darning, and muttered on the breath of a half-sigh.

"That's exactly the wife a man will want."

My father shot her a sharp look, his brow becoming rippled with lines and ever more furrowed. Making a lightning-swift estimation in my mind of how quickly he could reach for his danda (the only mental arithmetic that I could proclaim myself a master of), which lay on the other side of the room, I launched another question at him. "Look, are we actually getting a shop or is it more... I don't know... a box on wheels where we will sell scarves and burgers from on match days?"

"Scarves and burgers?" retorted Aftab, his acne-dotted face peering from above a copy *The Sun* newspaper. "I don't know what sort of shops you've been to lately. Mind you, you'd probably love somewhere that would sell both food and clothes all under the same roof."

"Why don't you take you and your high-literature there upstairs or at least to the other room? It's not as if we don't know why you look at that." I spat under my breath, speaking at twice the speed so as to go undetected from Mum and Dad.

"Don't be so cross, Mal," came Ferzana, bringing in a tray of biscuits from the kitchen and setting it down onto the table, shoving me from my spot on the sofa onto its arm, which was already dilapidated from having one too many siblings perch upon it. "You know Mum always takes a marker pen to page three anyway. She'd take a marker pen to Michelangelo's David if she could."

Despite it being the decade of mini-skirts, tight tops and songs like *Lay a Little Loving' on Me*, it wouldn't be too inaccurate to say that pretty much anything and everything that teetered on precipice of being risqué was strictly banned from our household. Indeed, my mother had perfected the art of springing off the sofa and diving over the table with the agility of an SAS commando, immediately changing the channel whenever a kissing scene happened to be on screen. Truth be told, although I was eighteen years of age I remained quite puzzled as to how the mechanics of producing offspring (as my mother would perhaps have put it had she ever dared to enter such dialogue) actually worked, and I highly doubted that Ferzana, who is two years my senior, had much of an idea either. Of course, were I ever to confront her on the matter she would deny any ounce of naivety. Apparently, she had a whole host of admirers – but then, to qualify as an admirer in Ferzana's book you only needed to be male, not a direct relative and within a five-mile radius of her. However, her claiming to have even slightest sense of worldly wisdom is no more an honest claim than a politician claiming to have moral integrity. It is a curious matter how decency always seems to belong to those who wish to reject it, and never to those who are desperately in need of it.

"I've not bought a shop – it's just a potential lead. Your uncle Javed told me that one of the old shops in Old Trafford might be coming up for leased usage in the next few years, and I'm thinking it could be a nice investment for the family," said Dad. My eyes rolled over to Mum, who continued to be engrossed in her task, slowly threading the needle over and over with gentle looped movements. Dad's words seemed to breeze past her as if they were nothing more than a mild flurry of wind – or better yet, hot air.

"And did you maybe think about who'd actually run this shop?" I asked, all the while keeping my eyes fixated on my mother's glaze look of disinterest.

"Well, we would of course, as a family," my Dad responded. My mouth hung slightly agape as one of my eyebrows shot into an arch – it was as if Mum's upwardly pulled thread had caught it along the way. Before I was able to ask but another question, Dad added, "I'm going to see the owner tonight, and talk about the possibilities. Mr Grey called, seems like a decent enough chap."

At the mere mention of a mister, Ferzana, who had mastered all linguistic articles designating male presence in French, Spanish, German and Arabic (her sole achievement from her Koran classes), put down the ginger nut that was midway enroute to her mouth and, with an almost auseous amount of enthusiasm, quipped, "I'll go with you, Dad, I'm a great judge of character!"

This time it was my father's turn to resist the urge to cock his eyebrow in profound cynicism, something he was much better at than me, given his eyebrows' distinctly unanimated quality. Knitted and at ease were pretty much the breadth of their expression. "Malika, you come with me. Ferzana, you can make the chapattis for dinner," he said, and before my self-esteem could inflate with thoughts of my Dad perhaps considering me a worthy second-in-command, he added, "Malika's entire chapattis end up square. She'll make a terrible wife."

As we sloped through Old Trafford, I gazed at the waxy yellow lights of the overhead street lamps and the dusty purple haze of the evening sky.

"Dad," I began, my hands wedged in the pockets of my puffer jacket. "Why do people make such a fuss about Pakistanis owning corner shops?"

"Because we're better businessmen, beti," he replied. Between us there was a moment's pause, the clatter of my sandals (yes, I happily risked frostbite on my tones for the sake of Asian fashion regulations) measuring the distance between his words and what would follow like a clumsy metronome.

"Do you think I'll make a good businesswoman?" I asked.

"Well, if you continue to make chapattis and tea as badly as you do, it might be the only option left for you," he said as we turned the corner.

MY DIARY

My diary is my loyal best friend
Into this mad shop we had to descend
So afraid in case my diary gets read
I have to hide my diary under my bed

Dad's big danda we all do dread
Just can't wait until I get wed
Want to be happy and so carefree
Hidden secrets in my private diary

Family and friends and the customers to
Each one helps, as there is much to do
Dad is the bully and Mum is our rock
Just remembered, my diary has no lock

This one year diary hides my inner fear
From Dad's bad temper we have to stay clear
Dad the gambler, with his large glass of beer
I am recording our happiness, love and each tear

January 2nd 1972

Bought my first diary

It was the colour that drew me – a romantic red, like a strawberry boiled sweet tempting me. It lay nestled in the depths of Reggie's Convenience Store – an Aladdin's Den of crayons, pens, and notebooks so poorly stacked they'd make a health inspector cry.

A soft velvet face, soon to be my best friend, my diary… and it only cost a shilling. I'd always wanted to be an author, a poet, a singer – I was destined to be a commentator on all things. I had thought Opportunity Knocks to be my path to success but I realised late that it was aptly named. I had waited, eyes wide and eager, like a castaway looking to the sky, almost driven insane, longing for a reply to my entry form. My buzzing hopes were abruptly swotted as my mother informed me that Dad had binned my application. I don't blame her or Dad. I'm not bitter. Honestly.

Mr. Hughie could go stuff himself though – I had found my platform of expression. It could fit just right in my clasped hands, as if it were holy water and, like water, my words would pour. I had my diary.

My childhood took place sometime between the decade of free love and the era of the Iron Lady. My family life was relatively typical: I was always the first one to get my elder sister's second-hand clothes – something I didn't envy, honest! Jeans were never designed to last two siblings over. I had a brother too but fortunately he was omitted from the clothing transition... just. Dad briefly thought that a tailored shalwar could look like a rather convincing set of plus fours. If it hadn't been for the darsee charging too much (too much being any figure of legal tender) Aftab would have been walking down Oxford Road in the finest polyester.

My dad was built like a tank, and his words could demolish you just as fast – waving a danda as a turret. But underneath that amour, there was actually a gentle streak. Mum, however, never wore a mask – her tears flowed like a stream when she watched her sad videos and drama. No one ever cared to tell her that it was just acting and that the singing lady wasn't really going to be banished from her family home for all eternity.

Ferzana is the elder of the sisters, she is very modern, rebellious and is very bossy, she likes to have the upper hand upon people! She has a slightly darker complexion than her siblings; her bonus is her big gob! She is petrified of Lucky, who is our family pet cat. If Ferzana ever tries to bully one of her siblings, Lucky is the dart which is aimed and thrown at Ferzana. Nevertheless, I have to admit Ferzana is the empathetic of the siblings; she has a heart of gold, she is also the temptress of the siblings and is more outgoing, elegant, stylish and self-centred. Ugh. At the moment she is the main driver in the family. She honestly thinks all the men fancy her! She continuously looks in the mirror at her so-called "God sent beauty!" Her downfall is her manic temper, just like Dad's horrid anger.

Miriam is our baby sibling. She is polite, chubby, jolly, hilarious and set in her little prying ways, but she can be very stubborn and can get on one's nerves at times. Her hobby is eating, she likes to eat and taste many sweets, chocolates and puddings.

The list can go on, no wonder she keeps putting the weight on.

Malika (that's me). I am the family counsellor, I weigh things up in every situation, judging what should and should not be done. I am the shop director, shopkeeper and my family's taxi driver to school and back. I am the stock keeper and the brain of the family all rolled into one. In other words, I am the main slave worker of Dad's shop, ha ha.

Aftab is the only brother. He is naive, susceptible and in many ways, he is intellectual and he can be mischievous, but we all love him, he would help any damsel in distress.

Even more, if the damsel is of a similar age to Aftab.

My dad, (Mr. Ali) is somewhat of an animal lover. His main love is horses, that is why he gambles on the horses at the local bookmakers. His other love of life is dogs; he adores the greyhound race track, betting most of his money on the dogs.

Dad is a very hot-tempered man, he is gossipy, bossy, very dominant and sometimes he hides from mum at a special place. That is where he would be drinking alcohol and playing darts at his local pub.

His downfall is his erratic behaviour, he moans so much that I am now convinced he is on the male menopause.

Mum (God bless her) would be up at dawn performing her usual ritual,

Cooking and cleaning in the morning, when breakfast was ready Mum would blow her long ear-splitting silver whistle, to wake everyone up for school and work.

Mum's morning habitual was almost complete, except for one more duty, her little garden which she tendered to with extreme love and care.

In the large black and white painted back yard were her little babies (her flowers) which were swaying away happily within the multi-coloured tubs. Within the small brown round tubs were her beautiful red roses, yellow daffodils, pink tulips and purple heather. At the rear was an enormous green wide tub, in which appeared to be a miniature apple tree, consisting of red rosy apples which were hanging from the branches. They looked so juicy and mouth-wateringly delicious that no one, except mum, was allowed to pick the apples in case we bruised her apples, or her tree (funny woman!).

Each day, with the exception of Sunday, Mum would wait tolerantly for the postman to distribute the letters, whilst praying that a letter would arrive from her family members in Pakistan. Oh my God what a lonely, dismal and dreary life Mum has.

The large, somewhat disorderly four-bedroom council house, in which my family and I had lived in for ten delightful years, was unique as well as having special sentimental value in our hearts. Within this happy house we had such ample memories, this house was part of our past and present, but the future was about to change for the better (well, that is what I had assumed).

My life was a little hectic, the reason being, I was studying for my A levels, then coming home and helping Mum with my hyperactive siblings.

When we all came home from school, Mum would have our meal ready for 4.30 p.m. every day except weekends. Soon after, Dad would come home from work and sternly tell his children to do their homework, whilst he told Mum the usual story for the day – how boring!

Aftab had been playing football with his school friends and had kicked the football accidently at a neighbour's car's wing mirror, all that could be heard were little pieces of cracked glass falling rapidly upon the wet muddy road.

Our neighbour John (his nickname is Gobby, wonder why?) rushed out of his house shouting furiously at the teenagers, then he crossly glanced upon Aftab. Without saying a word to Aftab, John furiously came knocking upon our door, my dad opened the door and said, "Hello Gobby, sorry I meant John, are you OK?"

John angrily said, "Your son has just kicked the football at my car and smashed my car wing mirror. I want the mirror replaced or I will phone the police."

Dad crossly said, "I will punish him, where is the bastard?"

Dad went into the kitchen to get hold of his danda (the danda was his favourite thick stick which he threatened people with). Well, Dad went over to Aftab, he grabbed Aftab by the collar and dragged him into the house. Dad slapped Aftab on the face and showed him the dreaded danda; it was not the slap on the face that frightened Aftab, it was the fear of the danda. Aftab was told off and was sent straight to bed.

Our other neighbours are Mr and Mrs McCarthy who have four teenage children; three sons and one daughter. Mr and Mrs McCarthy are about fifty years old, and in my opinion, I am sorry to say both racist. They do not allow their children to have foreign girlfriends or foreign boyfriends. Their daughter called Anne had secretly been dating an African man, whose name was Obama and he loved Anne so much and vice versa.

A few weeks later my dad was told by another nosy neighbour, a pensioner called Mrs Lawson, that Anne was pregnant and that she had eloped with her boyfriend Obama.

Anne's parents were furious and would never let her come back home again.

Well! That's what happens when one is racist.

January 5th 1972

The Shop

Dad was feeling irritable, lonely and somewhat low-spirited, so he decided to visit his brother Javed who lives in Old Trafford.

Dad had left his cigarettes and lighter at home, so he decided to walk to the nearest shop which was just across the road from his brother's house. This particular shop was beckoning Dad to come into its lion's den. The shop looked so eerie; with dimmed lighting it was a dark, mysterious curiosity shop.

Dad entered the shop vigilantly. He waited tolerantly to be served. He waited a few more minutes and then he curiously called out, "Hello, I have been waiting in this shop for a while now, could I have assistance please?"

There was a deadly silence, suddenly a somewhat pitiful cry was heard, followed by a loud moan. Then Dad peeped around the back of the shop and saw an elderly lady lying helplessly upon the floor; she looked somewhat confused and pale she was obviously in much discomfort. She cried hysterically, putting her arms in the air asking for help. Dad ran into the lounge and found an old brown strong large wooden chair. He helped the lady to sit upon the chair, and then he went into the old putrid kitchen and fetched back a cold glass of water to calm the distraught lady. She was very appreciative and thanked Dad wholeheartedly. Calmly she whispered, "My name is Mrs Grey, I felt so warm then a little dizzy, then suddenly without warning I collapsed upon the hard-wooden floor and I could not get myself up." Dad felt sorry for Mrs Grey and stayed with her for at least one hour to make sure she was alright. Dare I say it, Mrs Grey asked Dad if he knew anyone who would be interested in purchasing her most treasured grocery shop,

Mrs Grey pitifully said, "Due to my elderly and disabled condition, plus my severe arthritis and heart condition, I think the time is right to sell this family shop which has accommodation on top. Truly I will be sorry to leave this lovely busy shop, but I have no choice as my health is not what it used to be."

Dad said eagerly, "I will certainly let you know."

Mrs Grey thanked Dad for all the kind help he had given her, she even gave Dad, as a thank you gesture, two spotted dick cakes wrapped up in foil, plus a can of cold Coke.

Just before Dad departed from the shop Mrs Grey quickly wrote her telephone number onto a scrap of paper, in case Dad knew of anyone who wished to purchase her grocery shop.

Dad waved her goodbye, then off he went to his brother's house.

Upon arriving at Javed's three-bedroom terraced house, Dad rang the bell. His sixteen-year-old nephew opened the door to welcome his uncle inside, Dad told his younger brother about all the drama he had at Mrs Grey's grocery shop, they both had a natter then eagerly had a warm awaiting meal together, which consisted of meat curry, chapattis and plain yogurt.

The two brothers caught up on the latest gossip about their families and the scandal about their so-called friends and even their enemies.

After Dad had eaten his meal he had a well-earned rest and then made his way back home.

Dad came back home excitedly, he then paused for a second and asked us all inquisitively if we would be interested in purchasing a shop, with living accommodation on top.

Overwhelmingly I said, "Dad, let's go for it. I will leave my studies and become a full-time shop keeper." Believe me, those words uttered from my mouth were the biggest mistake of my entire life.

January 8th 1972

Dad decided to buy the shop

Everything went blissfully well. Dad had hastily bought the grocery shop, whilst taking a heavy mortgage upon his head.

Dad had told the elderly occupants that they could stay rent free for a few weeks, as long as they gave me work-experience, which they agreed to.

Upon entering the shop, I was a little anxious, as there to welcome me were two large old black and white twin beasts – shall we call them cats. The beasts looked up at me showing me their small sharp bloodthirsty fangs; they growled and hissed as they watched my every move. I was a little frightened but Mr and Mrs Grey reassured me that the cats were very friendly. Well, they could have fooled me!

Dad sent me to the grocery shop for training in the art of buying and selling. At first the training was so exhausting, it felt more like a chastisement.

Mr and Mrs Grey excitedly asked me if I would like to go to the cash and carry with them. I said, "I would love to go with you both, thank you."

Why did I utter those words from my silly little mouth.

Mr. Grey had a very large, ancient, rusty old battered green Ford Consul car.

The three of us sat comfortably in the shabby old car, whilst Mr. Grey drove to the nearest cash and carry.

Mr Grey, whilst driving had on several occasions nearly crashed into the cars in front of us, he kept jerking and stalling and besides that I nearly had a nervous breakdown.

The next incident was the worst I had ever experienced in my life.

Mr Grey drove so fast, almost like a racing driver around the roundabout and nearly had us all killed on the spot. We had a lucky escape, phew!

I had to breathe in slowly and very deeply. I had a severe panic attack. I was soon back to normal but unfortunately during that half an hour I must have gained half a head of grey hairs. Whichever driving instructor had passed a man like Mr Grey must have been sick in the head.

When we finally arrived at the cash and carry, I found the building to be enormous. We collected our large trolley and off we went, aisle after aisle, filling the trolley up with so many goods, including food tins, drink bottles and sweets. Yes, I was in heaven.

Many of the workers came to help us and would keep on talking to us.

Mr and Mrs Grey flippantly said, "Malika, looks like you have many admirers who work in this cash and carry."

I thought, whatever turns you elderly people on, ha ha. At least we arrived back at the shop in one piece, thank God.

Mr Grey asked if I had enjoyed my first day of work experience. I told him it was an experience I would never forget.

In the morning Dad had to go back to the shop, because the new board was ready to be erected high above the shop.

The long red and white sign had been erected. It read: ALI'S SHOP.

I could not remember a more honoured and privileged moment than seeing my dad's name outside high above his dream shop.

One week had passed and now the entire family was getting ready to move into Ali's Shop.

Our furniture was waiting to be removed and placed into the large removal van.

The large white, rusty and dirty dented removal van had finally arrived, then out came two enormous overweight men. They both smelled strongly of cigarettes, I think they had never heard of the word hygiene. They both came into our house and were astounded to see how much furniture there was to remove.

The furniture included one white rusty cooker, one large white fridge with no handle, four double beds, two dark brown antique wardrobes, with matching brown dressing tables, two matching blue lamp shades, one large oval glass coffee table and one battered old blue and white three-piece suite. The removal men were shocked upon looking at Mum's twenty heavy suitcases, plus odds and ends, but everything seemed to fit in the back of the large removal van.

Mum and Dad sat in the front passenger seats near the van driver. The driver's colleague sat in the large makeshift seat behind them, and guess where the rest of the family unwillingly sat? You guessed it, we all sat illegally at the back of the removal van. Some of the siblings sat on the sofa, whilst I sat on the dressing table, how uncomfortable and utterly degrading.

Well, we soon arrived at our destination after a bumpy ride, but during our journey poor Aftab was moaning he needed the toilet. He nearly wet his pants, poor lad.

It was more embarrassing when we had eventually reached our destination, and people were peeping out of their windows (from behind their dirty net curtains) watching the Asian family coming out of the removal van, one by one.

I was thanking God that we had all arrived at our destination safely.

Upon entering the small grocery shop, which (dare I say it) would be our prison for many years to come, now we had finally moved into Ali's Shop.

Moving the furniture to our approval took time; our hoover was even shocked as to how much dirt and dust there was to collect in all the bedrooms!

Once the cleaning process had finished, we could all get on with our lives, meaning duties and deliveries. I had to sort out everything, including where the food shelves would be displayed, plus going to the cash and carry and so on.

January 10th 1972

The first day

We all lived above the shop, my two sisters, including my handsome, witty brother. I peered slowly and nervously from my front bedroom window, hands twitching, as I pulled back the crisp white net curtain. There outside our shop a sight greeted me and completely took my breath away... The queue went to the bottom of the road. My heart started racing, thoughts swimming through my head: How am I going to cope? Will I have a panic attack? I was prone to anxiety, and panic attacks due to being bullied at school. I chose to leave school early when father had mentioned he was going to buy a shop.

Now I had my first job as a full-time shop keeper! I just could not wait.

I ran into Ferzana's bedroom the eldest of the sisters, screaming excitedly, "Get up and come and look outside my window." Ferzana was buried under her duvet. I crawled onto her bed, dragging her bedding off, demanding that she quickly get dressed.

Suddenly there was father's voice bellowing, "Hurry up and get down here, always bloody sleeping! Look, you know the shop is opening in thirty minutes."

Ferzana rushed into the bathroom quickly washing her face and putting lots of thick make-up onto her face to cover her spots, ugh!

A large box of creamy chocolates was left upon the shop counter for every new customer, it is a sign of good luck (well, that's what Dad had told us! ha ha).

We all quickly rushed down stairs and each one of us took our place for the official opening of Ali's Shop.

January 11th 1972

Miriam's sweets

My youngest sibling is my little chubby sister Miriam, she is so cute but greedy – she loves her food, especially sweets! She had set her eyes upon all the scrumptious different coloured sweets, some were red, brown orange and multi-coloured; there were many dark and milk flavoured chocolates. Her eyes rolled frantically with excitement.

She assumed she was in paradise; the truth being, Miriam had already tasted every chocolate and sweet imaginable in the shop, ugh! (It's not as if she was slim, far from it she is greatly obese, bless her.)

The following day Mum had asked Miriam to change her soiled smelly clothes, but Miriam was stubborn. She persistently moaned, "Mum, I don't want to change my clothes, I'll get changed later, and anyway you can't force me to get changed!"

Mum shouted loudly, "No, get your dirty clothes off now."

Miriam would not listen, so Mum decided to take Miriam's clothes of forcibly. Mum tugged and pulled, but still Miriam's dress would not come off.

Ferzana quickly joined in to help Mum, whilst Miriam wiggled and resisted. She still would not get changed, and then quite unexpectedly out of Miriam's clothing fell lots of small chocolate bars and sweets. Miriam cried hysterically as Ferzana quickly cuddled Miriam she placidly explained, "These chocolates and sweets are all ours, there was no need to hide them under your dirty clothing."

Miriam's tears quickly stopped, and she ecstatically said, "Ferzana, that means we can take as much chocolates and sweets for free from our shop. Great."

Miriam eagerly tucked into lots of chocolate bars, sticky sugary and sourly flavoured sweets, followed quickly by a can of Coke.

Dare I say it, Miriam felt so utterly sick, this incident taught her an important lesson, not to be too greedy. Oh, by the way, Miriam has since gone off sweets and chocolates. I wonder why? Ha ha.

January 14th 1972

Unwanted guests

The keys to our council house were ready to be given back to the council office, but unfortunately my dad received a phone call from his dear old friend Rahim Butt. He seemed troubled he said, "Salaam brother, hope you are well. I was just wondering if you can possibly help me. Brother, it is a big favour I am asking of you. I have a dear friend who is living in Scotland. His name is Shahid, he has fallen in love with the landlord's daughter and has secretly married her in a Muslim ceremony, he then eloped with his wife and stepson. Please can you somehow help them, as next week the family will be arriving in Manchester."

Dad respected his friend Rahim so he calmly said, "No bother, brother, I will do all I can to help them."

Rahim thanked Dad for his generosity and said, "The man's name is Shahid Khan, he will be arriving with his wife and stepson. Also, Shahid will be in touch with you very soon, thanks again."

One week had passed and sure enough, Shahid contacted Dad to tell him he would be arriving in Manchester at Piccadilly Train Station on Saturday at 4 p.m, along with his wife and his stepson. Dad told Shahid that he would be there to welcome them all, and would pick them up in his car. Well, here came another burden, Dad really put difficulty and stress upon our family.

Saturday soon arrived. It was 3.30 p.m., Dad got

ready, then asked me to drive him to Piccadilly Train Station.

Upon arriving at the train station, I waited patiently in the car whilst Dad walked in to receive our guests. Half an hour later Dad was back accompanied by a man who was short, dark-skinned and a bit scruffy looking; his wife Shabnam had a bit of a limp and a terrible nervous stutter. Much to Dad's dismay he could not understand most of her speech. Shabnam had a child from a previous marriage who was about eight years old; he looked anxious but really excited.

As the guests sat in my car, I said, "Salaam walakum" and they all said, "Walakum Salaam". I casually looked at Shahid, and I knew in my heart that he had married a disabled woman to get his indefinite stay in this country. I could see no love in his eyes for his wife, but many people would sell their souls to live in this country. I felt so sorry for his wife, that she could not see through this devious, cunning man.

Dad told me to drive back to the shop as Mum had prepared a lovely meal for our problematic guests, sorry I mean our most unfortunate welcome guests.

Mum waited patiently for her guests to arrive. Once they had arrived Mum welcomed the guests with open arms into the dining room. (Mum knew the guests must be hungry as they had travelled all the way from Scotland.)

Mum had cooked a delicious, mouth-watering meal, consisting of kebabs, meat biryani, pakoras and chicken curry, dhal and for dessert, rice pudding, yummy.

31

After the meal, we all sat down in the living room so we could get acquainted, then Dad casually said, "Malika, I still have the keys to the other house, can you drive us all there? They will be our guests for a couple of weeks."

Arriving back at our empty cold house, the guests made themselves at home. They knew there was much cleaning to do, but they had no rent or bills to pay. Dad told them he would pay the rent until they found another place.

We all know that nowadays this world is a selfish place to live in, but Dad has a heart of gold and would probably help anyone in need.

Shahid and his wife were coming to visit us nearly every day. Dad did not mind and if he did mind he never showed it.

One week had blissfully passed by, then Shahid and Shabnam strolled into our shop panicking and distressed. Dad was concerned he said, "Shahid, what has happened?"

Shahid said, "The Oldham police have contacted me, and told me that cars are being spot checked on the roads, by the road traffic police, and one car in particular was stopped. It was a black Honda Civic and inside there were five Asian men, their ages ranging from eighteen to forty. The policeman was frozen to the spot when he saw what was in the boot! There was a small gun, two three-foot-long swords, three club hammers, five baseball bats and seven choppers. The policeman radioed through requiring assistance, and upon the arrival of the other police officers, each man was handcuffed. One by one they were interrogated and each man was questioned by detectives.

It was later that they found out Shabnam's brother had paid these villains to murder Shabnam and her family, Ali, I don't know what to do? I am only a visitor in this country, please help us." Shahid started to cry pitifully. Dad was very concerned about getting involved, especially with these Asian gangsters, but still he offered to take Shahid and his family to the Oldham police station.

Dad asked me to drive him to Oldham and to collect Shahid and his family on the way.

Driving on the motorway was a little frightening because the weather was very windy

And the rain was crashing down upon my windscreen.

We all reached Oldham safely, then quickly made our way to the police station.

Shahid and Shabnam were questioned separately, each giving separate statements, whilst Dad and I had to wait, bored, for over two hours in the waiting room.

Soon husband and wife came out of the interviewing room, both were silent and upset.

Dad did not ask anything or say anything, he let them have their peace.

Whist driving the family to their home, Shahid confessed, telling Dad that the rogues may be getting many years in prison, and Shabnam's brother had been arrested in Scotland. Dad said "Leave it all up to Allah, as Allah is the all hearing and all seeing. Allah is the bigger planner."

Shahid was to later find out that all the five men who were paid and on a mission to come and kill him and his family had been sentenced to twelve years each in prison for their involvement in this terrible planning.

Dad phoned his dear friend Rahim, and told him everything that had happened with his so-called friend Shahid, and that he had to give the keys back to the council.

A few months had passed, still the unwanted guests had not found another suitable accommodation to move to. (Let's face it, which person in their right mind would want to leave an all-inclusive free house?) This couple were very cunning and manipulating, but Dad had enough of their capers.

Dad had been paying the rent to the council for this semi-detached house. Dad's temperament was becoming very moody and he complained to Mum, saying furiously, "This is the last time I help anyone. Everyone wants help, I have my own family to support. I already took a loan out to buy this shop, what do people think that I am? A rich millionaire?" Dad walked off in a rage and sulked in the lounge.

Four months had passed, and Dad decided he had to become stern with the unwelcome visitors as he did not want to pay any more rent; he wanted to give the keys back to the council.

Dad caught the bus to our council house and kept ringing the bell as he knew Shahid and his family were in the house. Eventually Shahid nervously opened the door and called Dad into the house.

Dad moodily said to both of them, "Look, you have been in this house for many months. I only took you in the house for a few weeks, out of the kindness of my heart, and I do not even know who you are? I have shown you much mercy, now look you are taking bloody liberties. You have to move from this house because in two weeks – I am going to give the keys back to the council."

Later Dad said in an irritable manner "goodbye" whilst slamming the door behind him. Looks like Dad is going a bit loony, heaven help us!

A few weeks later Dad went back to the council house. He felt so incredibly happy, that the unwanted guests had left the house, not even a card of thank you for helping them so much. Dad would never help anyone in this terrible situation again.

Dad took the keys back to the council office, and as for Shahid and family, they were nowhere to be seen. The couple had probably gone to use some other mug to help them with their fake crying tears. Helping is one thing but using people for their own benefit is another thing. Goodbye to rubbish.

January 21st 1972

Desi food

Dad had woken up early in the morning, the reason being he wished to buy some Asian Desi food which included spices, flour and rice for all our customers.

Dad shouted, "Malika, come on hurry up. Haven't you painted your face yet? You know we have to buy lots of Desi food. You're not listening to me, now hurry up!"

Confused I said, "Dad, what do you mean, Desi food?"

Dad looked at me in disgust saying, "What have you been eating all these years, meat curry, chicken curry, chapattis and pakoras etc. We have to get the ingredients for the curries, some large packets for your mum and some small packets for our customers."

I quickly drove my nagging, irritable dad to "Ahmed's Cash and Carry" in Stockport.

Upon entering the gigantic cash and carry, I could see lots of Asian food. The aroma was enchanting, the wonderful whiff of the spices made my mouth water. Dad was so motivated that he rushed around with the large metal trolley; inside the trolley he put a box of twenty curry powder packets, followed by chilli powders, cumin seeds, turmeric powder, garam masala and so the list went on.

Dad's eyes saw the large yellow packets of besan (gram flour) with which pakoras are made.

He picked up six large packets of besan, he picked up a large bag of Patna rice for Mum which would last us a few months! Dad also picked up ten small bags of basmati rice for the customers (typical Dad, getting cheap rice for his family). Dad also put twelve cans of chick peas, eight spinach tins, ten black eyed beans all in the metal trolley which by now looked full.

Dad's eyes then looked towards the chapatti flour – he bought a large bag of wholemeal chapatti flour for Mum, and some small packets of medium chapatti flour for the customers.

I felt a bit alarmed thinking we have not, as yet, had any Asian customers come into our shop!

Angrily, I said to Dad, "Why are you buying all these spices and Asian foods? We don't get that many Asian customers coming into our shop."

Dad moaned, "Don't you think beside Asian people, that English people and other foreigners love Asian food, like curries chapattis and pakoras? Malika, please think before you speak."

I don't think Dad has left me much of a brain to think with!

I felt as though I had been at Ahmed's Cash and Carry for several hours. I dreaded putting away all the stock upon the shelves .

We soon arrived back at the shop. I pressed the car horn, then Ferzana and Aftab and the rest of the family came out to help fetch the stock into the shop. Dad told us he would display the Asian food the next day upon an old shelf he had found, as he was tired and in need of a rest.

I told Ferzana to take over whilst I have a well-deserved cup of Kashmiri milk tea, yummy, and a little relaxation (if that was at all possible, ha ha).

January 22nd 1972

The two ladies

Dad was happily whistling away. He put a large white shelf upon the shop wall using odd hinges and screws and a small sign up which simply read 'Asian Desi Food'.

Then he quickly organised where all the Asian food should be displayed upon the shelf.

First, he put the six small bags of white rice on the left side of the shelf; next to the rice he put five small chapatti packets, then four lentil packets, four poppadum packets, eight curry powder packets, and six channa tins. Dad wanted to make sure our customers could see the Asian food which he had so lovingly displayed. Whilst giggling I said to Dad, "Who's going to buy the Asian groceries? Dad, only English people live in this area."

Dad looked at me up and down, whilst giving me an angry look. He loudly moaned, "Look, don't be a clever dickie with me. English people love the taste of Asian food and rice and curries, and they know how much a small portion of curry costs at the bloody restaurants."

I completely ignored dad, just thinking, silly old man, he must be dreaming.

Four days had passed, then into the shop walked two smartly dressed young ladies. One of the ladies quickly pointed to the Asian Desi Food sign. At first, I thought the ladies were joking amongst themselves, then suddenly they were picking up different Asian food from the shelf.

I thought in my heart, well Dad must not be going senile after all, ha ha. The groceries were put upon the counter, rice, chapatti flour, poppadum's, and much more.

One of the ladies excitedly said, "Oh! It's fantastic that you sell Asian food, as we have to travel to Wilmslow Road to get these groceries. Thank you."

The ladies paid for their goods and walked merrily out of the shop, with their heavy bags of shopping.

Dad gave me such a cheeky look as if to say, I told you so. Silence speaks louder than words, yes! Dad won me over, God bless him.

January 23rd 1972

The two chickens

Dad had gone out with his dear friend Yacoob, to get some stock.

Just a few hours later he came back into the shop, holding a large brown box. I could hear strange noises coming out of the box, and Dad excitedly said, "Look, I have bought two live chickens, now I am going to put them in the cellar to let you all play with them. Treat them like your pets!"

I quickly told Aftab and Miriam to come down to the cellar. Dad had bought us two chickens as pets. Miriam had a handful of rice to feed the chickens, Aftab had some bird seed and, I had a small bowl of water in case the chickens were thirsty.

We crept quietly down the wobbly old staircase, and spent twenty minutes playing with the brown clucking chickens whom we had named Peter and Paul. The chickens kept following us around – we gradually grew to love Peter and Paul.

Our pets had been with us for four weeks and they were getting fatter and fatter. Dad seemed somewhat excited. He asked me to serve the customers in the shop, so I took over the usual duties. Dad said he was going down into the cellar to check on the chickens.

Dad had disappeared for over twenty minutes, so I asked Aftab to come into the cellar with me and feed the chickens. We quietly walked down the wobbly steps into the cellar whilst carrying the bird food.

What we saw shocked us, as there in front of us were two headless chickens with blood dripping from their necks – they were running about headless Oh, my God.

Aftab let out a scream. I screamed louder. We realised Dad had bought the chickens for our family to eat, and they were never meant to be our pets. Aftab ran into the bathroom and vomited in the sink.

Dad chopped, cleaned and washed the chickens, and then he gave them to Mum to cook a delicious chicken curry.

Believe me, none of us ate the chicken curry. We bought fish and chips from the chip shop.

As far as the rest of the family were concerned, Dad could eat his chicken curry for four consecutive days all by himself, ugh!

January 26th 1972

The accountant

Perspiration was flowing down my face, it had been such a long, busy tiring day. It was finally time to lock the shop, but I did not finish there, it's now time to start my next duty, cleaning the shop and mopping the floor and then it's my favourite time when I get to go and retire to my bed as it gets so exhausting running Dads prison shop, oops I meant *Ali's Desi Shop*.

The floor had virtually dried, then all of a sudden I heard a gentle tapping upon the shop window. I looked, I listened, to my surprise there were two faces gazing back at me outside the window. They were of Asian origin. I opened the door and asked them politely, "Yes! Can I help you, is everything alright?"

The lady and man asked if they could buy some goods – they had just moved from Liverpool to Manchester, and had bought a house around the corner, in Cromwell Street.

The lady smiled, she was so grateful that I had opened the shop for them,

Softly and politely she said, "My name is Naureen. Thank you so much for opening the shop for us, we were panicking. We do not know the area too well, we only need bread, milk, tea bags sugar and a packet of porridge, please."

Well what could I say, at least the shop floor was dry, plus they would become our new customers. I asked her if the gentleman with her was her father. She said,

"No, he is my husband." Dare I say it, I put my foot in it again. I don't know when to shut my stupid mouth.

I opened the shop door to let the couple out, Naureen turned around and thanked me again. She said, "Anytime you need an accountant, Jamal is always there for you all." I thanked Naureen, then locked the door, switched off the fluorescent lights and locked the adjoining door to the shop.

Naureen and her husband Jamal became our regular customers. They both would come into the shop and have a homely chat with me and my family.

Jamal loved his Asian food, especially his meat biryani. My mother smiled whilst happily

Saying, "Naureen, my daughter makes the best meat biryani. Any time you need help to cook your biryani, my daughter will help you cook a tasty biryani."

The next day, sure enough, Naureen came to see Mum, seeking permission to take me to help her cook the perfect biryani.

A few hours had passed and Naureen's biryani was cooked. The aroma was wonderful, plus Naureen gave me a large plate of meat biryani to take home for my dad. Dad was so excited. Naureen's biryani was absolutely delicious.

January 28th 1972

One of my favourite customers

Doris is one of my dearest customers, she is always dressed so smart, her make-up is immaculate, and upon her large lips she applies bright red glossy lipstick. Doris's slightly grey hair is always neatly tied back into a tidy bun.

Doris always looks so pretty – she reminds me of the late actress Marilyn Monroe.

Every day Doris comes into our shop for her groceries and we usually have a lovely chat. This particular day Doris came into the shop looking extremely lonely and sad, as though she needed a friend to talk to, I asked her if everything was alright. She knew I was her listening ear.

She anxiously said, "There are a lot of problems going on which I will tell you about some other time." Then she sadly left the shop.

Doris seemed to be deteriorating rapidly; she looked thin, weak and stressed.

One Saturday evening, Doris's son Mike came into the shop. Mike was of small build he was grossly thin, had messy long ginger hair, and he smelt strongly of alcohol and urine. My stomach churned at the sight and smell of him, ugh. Mike told me he was very concerned about his mother, who he had been phoning since that afternoon, and his mother was not answering the telephone. I also tried phoning Mike's mother but still there was no answer.

Mike said, "Thanks, Malika, but I will try phoning Mother once again and ring her door bell again."

Mike then went on his way looking very concerned.

In the morning Doris came nervously into the shop, I told her that Mike had come in the day before and was very worried about her. Doris wept and inaudibly said, "Malika, I saw Mike outside my door. I was peeping from behind the curtains. I was too frightened to open the door to my son, because he has mental health problems. He can become very aggressive and as you know, he is an alcoholic. I phoned the hospital due to his mental ill health and they sent an ambulance which promptly came, and I saw Mike willingly going into the ambulance."

I told Doris that I was so sorry to hear about Mike's mental health condition. Doris put her head down whilst tears rolled down her wrinkled heartbroken face, then she went despondently on her way.

A week had passed and Doris had not set foot into our shop.

Two weeks had now passed, then into the shop walks Doris's younger sister Joan. She said sadly, "My sister Doris collapsed on the pavement. She was taken to hospital. As you know, Doris had been feeling unwell for a quite a long time. The doctors have done tests and she has been diagnosed with stomach cancer."

Upon hearing what Joan had said, my heart felt so low. I knew there something wrong with her, because Doris had been losing so much weight. There was nothing I could do but pray for her from the bottom of my heart.

A few weeks later Joan had popped into the shop to give me the distressing news that her sister Doris had passed away the day before, in her sleep. God bless her.

January 31st 1972

My old school friend

One Monday morning, I was just cleaning as usual, when a rather nervous well-dressed young woman walked into the shop. She asked with a strong Irish accent, "Morning love, do you sell whisky?"

I said, "Sorry, we don't sell alcohol, you will have to go to the supermarket across the road."

The young woman was smirking, she looked me up and down and with a gleam in her eyes, she said, "I seem to recognise your husky voice, are you Malika Ali?"

I looked strangely at her, replying, "Yes I am, how do you know my name?"

The young woman laughed and said, "Don't you recognise me? I am Sally O'Connor – you used to protect me in junior school and you sorted out the bullies who teased and hit me."

Giggling, I said, "You were that little spoilt rich girl, who the other kids were jealous of and that's why they picked on you, your parents gave you everything."

Sally put her head down in shame and said, "Truly, I am wealthy and rich, yes! I have everything yet I have nothing, but the Whiskey helps." I told her that anybody would love to be in her position and asked her why she had turned to alcohol.

Sadly, Sally said, "When my beautiful mother died my world fell apart. My mother was my world, now in life I can't be arsed."

Unfortunately, I did not realise that my nosy dad was listening, whilst standing in the passage corridor. He had heard everything!

Sally said that she would go to the supermarket across the road, and if they don't sell whisky, then dopily she said, "I can't be arsed, I will just go home. I will come to see you again." Sally waved goodbye and went on her way.

I felt so sorry for Sally, such a nice young woman and so lonely. Then suddenly Dad rushed quickly into the shop. Angrily, he said, "Why do you speak to that woman too much. Look at the way she speaks she keep saying can't be arsed. Why she kept saying such words 'can't be arsed'! Is she lesbian or homo going on about arse, don't mix with these type of women, then you will start to speak like her. Remember your dad's words, bloody keep going on about 'arse'."

Then Dad muttered to himself and walked into the living room to drink his favourite Punjabi tea. The only words I could think of in my heart were, 'Dad, have some feelings', but I dare not tell Dad as I would not want to be picked up and thrown over the other side of the counter with much of my bones broken, ha ha.

February 1st 1972

The dirty old man, Mr Groden

Becoming a fulltime shopkeeper, I had found that shop duties were very tiring and exhausting (especially when you're not paid any wages at all) but everyone in our family assisted in the serving and cleaning of our prison Shop.

There was one particular customer, an elderly, shabby, smelly man, he must have been in his late seventies – his name is Mr Groden. Mr Groden has wide beady bloodshot eyes, that could look deep and devilishly into one's soul. He actually made my skin crawl, he undressed me with his dirty shady-looking eyes. He had a stubble, a double chin and a habit of picking his nose, ugh! Even his nails were long and dirty; his sly grin made me shiver. He always wore his black, baseball cap (which was torn and very noticeable) upon his sweaty head.

My dad took a profound interest in this man – the reason being he could repair most cars. My car was always giving me problems and Dad was known for being mean with his money – he would always ask Mr Groden to fix my car. Mr Groden gave me the creeps, as whilst he was repairing my car, his beady eyes would look up at me from outside the shop window.

There was one particular incident when Mr Groden was fixing my car, he had actually taken the engine out, repaired it and put it back into the car. My dad gave Mr Groden only twenty pounds, he was so

shocked as well as angry. He was disgusted at the
twenty pounds Dad had given him for five hours of
work on my car.

Mr Groden grumpily said to me, "Malika, your
dad is a scrooge he has given me Victorian wages."
What could I say or do? That was my dad for you – a
scrooge in every way.

If anyone dare argue with my dad they would feel
his wrath, as many people before Mr Groden would
tell you! From abusive words to a quick hard punch,
Dad will never change, God bless him.

One serene evening, I was having a quick break from
the usual hectic routine in the shop, I was casually
tucking into my chocolate biscuit and my well-earned
warm cup of tea. Dad swiftly came into the lounge,
very excited, and with a gleam and twinkle in his eyes
he cheekily said, "Malika, there is a gentleman in the
shop, he has come to ask for your hand in marriage.
He is all dressed up and the rest is up to you my
daughter, it's either a yes or a no!"

Innocently I asked Dad who wants my hand in
marriage, but dad would not tell me. I patiently and
excitedly got up and peeped into the shop. There was
Mr Groden, all dressed up in a dark blue pinstripe suit
which was surprisingly well ironed, he was carrying a
large bunch of red roses and a black and white
patterned box of dark chocolates in his dirty grubby
hands. I turned around and looked at Dad, who by
now was giggling like a child. I think Dad thought he
was some kind of born comedian. I did not find this
situation amusing.

Coming back to my senses, I quietly and impatiently told Dad to get rid of this dirty old man, because he made me feel sick. Mr Groden went away a very unhappy old man and as for Dad, he had never laughed so much in his life. I had never felt so disgusted in my life, thank God, I never saw that sick dirty old man again.

February 4th 1972

Ferzana decides to clean the shop window

Dad was moaning, as usual, about the large shop window and the wooden frame being very filthy. Ferzana looked at Dad very calmly as she said, "Dad, leave the cleaning of the shop window to me. Calm down, let me put my make-up on, then I will clean the window and frame within an hour. Now let me get ready." Dad suddenly stopped his moodiness and bickering, and then he quickly went into the sitting room to rest.

Ferzana tried her best to get ready swiftly! We are talking about within an hour! When she had finished her face painting she rushed downstairs looking very immaculate. She looked absolutely stunning, her make-up was thickly painted upon her beautiful skinny face, her false eyelashes were thicker than normal, her clothes were a bit too tight fitting – her dark blue jeans looked as though they would rip at any time – her clinging red and gold T- tea shirt looked a bit too sexy, meaning the neck line was way too low. I thought to myself 'Ferzana you are only cleaning the flipping window, you are not on the catwalk modelling the latest fashion'.

Ferzana picked up a large green bottle of window cleaner spray, along with a large yellow dishcloth. She then went behind the shop counter and got the wooden chair. She climbed quickly, lifting herself on top of the small low fridge, then she hopped upon the heavy shelf which was attached to the bottom of the shop window.

I had on many occasions noticed Ferzana liked to spend extra time tidying and cleaning the shop window. She would sway her hips erotically left then quickly right many times over, as though she was doing a Hawaiian dance. (It was as if she was beckoning and hurrying the customers to come inside the shop to spend their money). Ferzana smiled then winked as she said, "You have to know how to play the game."

The young men and the dirty old men were walking past the shop then quickly reversing, as they rushed into the shop to buy something (even though they did not need anything). Some people were spontaneously buying cat food, but later on admitting that they didn't own a cat; others were buying nappies when they didn't have any children. The customers were obsessed and just wanted to take a closer look at Ferzana's exotic bottom. Truly, Ferzana was getting the customers flocking into the shop.

Ferzana winked at me. Giggling, she said, "Malika, let me tell you, I am not naive or docile like you. As I told you I know how to play this winning game, look at the customers rushing into the shop."

Unfortunately, I had to serve the kinky customers, who, once again, kept looking at Ferzana's figure and bottom moving to and fro. (Oh, how embarrassing). "Ferzana, I think it's time you change your wild rude behaviour and live a simple, cool and calm way of life"

"Well at least dad will be ecstatic that we have been so busy today with all the new customers and the increased shop takings"

"Oh, Ferzana, I am just frightened if Dad finds out about your seductive behaviour, you will be seeing stars before your eyes, if he decides to hit you with his famous danda". Within my heart, I know my sister will never change her ways.

As the saying goes – You can't live with them, and you can't live without them.

February 9th 1972

My driving test

I had been having driving lessons for many months now, and my instructor had told me that my driving test was coming up very soon. I hated driving but unfortunately, I had no choice; I had to somehow pass my driving test to help Dad bring back the stock from the Cash and Carry. I also had another duty, which was to drive my siblings to school and bring them back home again.

My first driving instructor, Peter, was a stout, middle-aged, short and miserable man. He was an idiot who wasted my time and wasted my dad's money. Whilst teaching me to drive he would stop the car to get out and do his wife's shopping, plus the other odd jobs he had to do during my driving lesson time.

Peter had put me in for my driving test, the silly man honestly knew that I was not yet an experienced driver. Guess what, I failed my driving test. I wonder why?

Dad took me to another driving school. There was a new sensible, strict instructor called Dave.

Dave was marvellous. He was a tall, handsome, middle-aged man and he spoke with a strong Scottish accent. Dave was so professional (unlike Peter) and he did not waste my driving lessons. I felt so confident with this driving instructor.

It was a Friday and the time had come to take my driving test. I prayed for it to be a lucky day for me. I felt confident (even though I was ill, with a chesty cough, and bad cold).

The examiner came, he sat comfortably next to me and told me what to do. I drove, I reversed I did my three-point turn, I correctly answered his questions and guess what? I passed my driving test. Whoopee, hurray! I felt as though I had won the lottery.

Upon arriving back at the driving centre, I saw Dave who was waiting patiently for me. He was over the moon and congratulated me. I thanked him for all his support.

When I had finally arrived back at the shop, Dad was waiting patiently behind the counter. He could see many tears in my eyes and gave me a big comforting hug, reassuring me everything would be alright. Lovingly, he said to me, "Don't worry Malika, there will always be another time to do your driving test."

I looked at Dad and smiled. Happily, I said, "Dad, I have passed my driving test."

Dad kissed me on my head (that loving moment in time will always be with me for the rest of my life). Dad asked me why I had tears in my eyes. I told him I had a very bad cold.

From that day, my life had completely changed. I was a shopkeeper bringing stock in for the shop, plus a taxi driver for my family – taking my siblings to school and back, taking mum's friends back to their houses, what a hectic life. As the saying goes, "such is life".

February 17th 1972

Whilst sitting bored in the shop, I wrote a little poem.

Ali's Prison Shop

This shop is open from nine till nine
We only sell food, we don't sell wine

Feeling bored and full of strife
For a bright young woman, this is no life

All I do is clean and serve
This type of life I do not deserve

All Dad does is argue and moan
About the bills and about his loan

Dad bought this shop, but the burden I have carried
Just can't wait until the day I get married

No rest at all and no time to stop
Just can't wait to get out of Ali's Prison Shop

February 21st 1972

The coal man

Every two weeks, Sam, our lovely coal man, would come into our shop delivering the usual twenty small bags of coal. Sam could lift three bags of coal on his strong muscular right shoulder – poor man, it's a miracle he did not have one shoulder shorter than the other. Sam is such a jolly man, full of funny jokes as well as being a well-mannered person.

He is short and stocky, he has muscles as big as melons, his cheeks are as red as strawberries. Upon his head he has a receding patch, plus his hair over time had slowly turned grey. His ears looked like the version of the cartoon figure Dumbo the elephant, and he always had a huge smile upon his face, God bless him. His dark, baggy black trousers would be half way down his large saggy bottom. I'm sure he wore them low on purpose, ha ha.

Sam is a caring man and he always bought Mum and Miriam a couple of large chocolate doughnuts. I am sure just to make them fatter, ha ha. Whenever Sam came into the shop he always knew there would be a nice warm cup of tea and a few custard cream biscuits waiting for him.

Soon Sam had to stop the coal bags. In replacement, he had to deliver smokeless coal which did not leave smoke. Things were changing for the better for the environment.

Unfortunately, just one month later, Dad received a

phone call from Sam's manager, John Watkin. John sadly said, "Mr Ali, I have some sad news about Sam. Whilst Sam was delivering some smokeless coal bags to a shop in Stretford, he started experiencing severe chest pains and fell on the hard-concrete floor. He banged his head and had a heart attack. He died on the spot."

Dad expressed his condolences to John, whilst also asking him to pass on our condolences to Sam's family.

When we found out about Sam, we were all completely shocked and upset, as Sam was such a pleasant and respectable caring man. We prayed for his family and God rest his soul.

February 22nd 1972

My admirer's red rose

Ferzana had put on her yellow rubber gloves – she was adamant to clean the top shelves behind the counter of the shop. The real reason for the gloves was that she hated her nails getting dirty or chipped whilst cleaning.

I was left to serve the customers. A few minutes later Sammy, a regular customer, walked in.

Sammy is an Asian man; he is tall, dark and overweight. Whenever he came into our shop you could smell petrol on his clothes, which absolutely smelt the shop out (this pong would disgust any customer). He is one of the mechanics who had fixed my dad's car on numerous occasions. I wouldn't say Sammy is handsome but even so, he thought he was a ladies man, ugh.

On this particular day, Sammy came singing into the shop, whilst he was holding in his right hand a single red rose. He came to the counter, then looked romantically into my eyes. He tried lovingly to give me the red rose. I put my head down and politely declined, whilst Ferzana started to uncontrollably laugh out loudly at him.

Sammy felt utterly humiliated he angrily rushed out of the shop slamming the door loudly behind him.

Once again Ferzana giggled as she said, "I think he really fancies you." I asked her why. Ferzana said,

"You're not that thick! Don't you know what a single red rose means? It means 'I love you'."

Confused and angry I shouted at Ferzana, "He is a married man with two children, he should be ashamed of himself. Well, that is one customer I will not be serving again. I will leave Dad to serve him next time, as Dad will give him more than a red rose. I can do without admirers like him, ugh! I am fed up, not hard up."

A little while later Dad came into the shop. He started to clean the fridge, whilst moaning, as usual. I carried on serving the customers, then two young teenagers of a shabby appearance came into the shop. They were sister and brother, and whilst I was not looking, the sister put a can of lemonade inside her dirty torn black trousers. Dad saw what the girl had done, he got hold of his danda, then angrily said to her, "Get that can of lemonade out of your trousers or I will get the can out for you."

The girl was shocked. She took out the can and apologised to Dad and said, "I will never steal from this shop again!"

After that incident, the young girl still came into our shop to buy sweets and groceries. Believe me, she never stole from our shop again.

February 29th 1972

The Chinese man and his illegal watches

Aftab excitedly asked Mum if she would like to go to a restaurant for a meal today, instead of slaving over the cooker for us all each and every day. Mother was ecstatic as she said, "Fantastic, but let's take Malika and Miriam with us."

Aftab said, "Alright, you're the boss, Mum."

Mum nervously asked Dad if he could look after the shop with Ferzana for a couple of hours, but Ferzana's face turned pale. She was not happy about this situation; she wanted to come along to the restaurant with us. Dad crossly told Ferzana to let the rest of the family go and that she must stay with him to look after the busy shop.

Well, Dad's words are the last words and have to be obeyed; he is the master of the family and he has spoken so we have no choice but to listen, ha ha.

I calmly waited in the car for Mum to come and sit in the front passenger seat, whilst Aftab and Miriam were sat comfortably upon the back seats. Everyone was now ready in the car, then off I cheerfully drove to Arshad's Restaurant.

We had all finally reached our destination, and I parked in the restaurant's enormous car park, which is based in Stockport. Upon entering the very busy restaurant, everything was so eye-catching; the beautiful lights were dimly lit, the exotic colourful flowers were stunning, and the large golden vases were exquisite, the music was calm yet serene, but the main thing was I had two hours away from the prison shop. At last, some freedom, ha ha.

We had to order our meal as the waiter waited patiently for Mother to make up her mind what she wanted to order. At the same time, Mother was chewing rapidly upon her false teeth, ugh! Mother excitedly said, "I think I will have two chicken kebabs, one meat samosa, one naan, a little salad and yogurt and a glass of lemonade, thanks."

Next, Miriam placed her order. She eagerly said, "A large portion of chips, four chicken kebabs, one samosa, a small donner kebab, no salad, two naans and yogurt, and a glass of Coke, and that's it, thanks."

Aftab then ordered his meal. He mildly said, "Could I please have a chicken curry, two meat kebabs, and two naans, yogurt with red hot chilli sauce and a glass of lemonade. That's it, thank you."

Next came my order. I was so hungry that my stomach was rumbling loudly. I quickly said, "I will have a large portion of donner kebab and one naan, salad and yogurt and one meat samosa, and a glass of limeade with a slice of lemon on top, thank you."

We all waited patiently for our food to be delivered upon the beautifully decorated table.

Ten minutes had passed, then into the restaurant walks this tall Chinese man. Upon his head he was wearing a black cowboy hat, and he carried a heavy satchel upon his back. He came up to our table and impatiently said, "Come on goody, goody new one. I have DVDs, watches, rings you want to buy cheap. Buy four items and I give you one free." Aftab looked up and down at the Chinese man, thinking is he for real?

Aftab annoyingly said, "No, thanks."

The Chinese man looked frustrated at not making a sale. He stopped and took one step in my direction, then he took off his cowboy hat using his right hand. He then stretched his left arm forward and pointed his left index finger in my face, and in a loud broken English voice he said, "SHE KNOW ME. Yes! She know me just ask her, she know me."

For some odd strange reason, he kept repeating these words three times. It was so embarrassing, particularly with the restaurant being full of diners. All I could hear and see were people pointing, smirking and laughing. This felt like one of the worst days of my life, I just wanted to go and hide under a stone. Truly, this was the only time I had wished I was back at Ali's Prison Shop. I calmly said, "No thanks, I don't wish to buy any watches or rings. Probably next time."

The Chinese man left miserably without making any sale. He was so upset that he rudely slammed the restaurant door behind him. The diners looked towards my family as they were shocked and disgusted at the behaviour of the Chinese man. Aftab shook his head in disbelief. He was disappointed with me, especially because I was the backbone of the family. Aftab gloomily said, "Malika, these watches and rings are illegal copies, plus you can get heavily fined."

I sadly said, "Aftab, this Chinese man usually comes every two weeks to our shop to sell me jewellery, as well as watches. I did not know that it was illegal to buy these items, but I promise, Aftab, I will never buy any more illegal items from him again."

Well, I couldn't complain. At least the meal was lovely; we were all full happy and contented, but Mother bought some naans and kebabs for Dad and Ferzana, just in case they moaned that we had not bought any food back for them.

Well, from that day to this, I had never bought any more illegal copies of anything, especially watches and rings. If Dad had found out he would have gone mad, especially with his famous danda trembling for another hit, but that mainly only happens on certain occasions, ha ha.

March 2nd 1972

Dad's cousin, Bashir

Dad and Uncle Bashir

Dad's ignorant cousin Bashir came to visit us. He was singing loudly whilst swaying into our shop.

Uncle Bashir is tall, fair-skinned and has blue overwhelmingly desirable eyes. He is very handsome and always wore a blue pinstriped suit. For some unusual reason Uncle Bashir never had any money in his pocket.

All the family knew he was a ladies' man, but most of the time he was a drunk and a professional gambler. He would always come to borrow money off Dad, but unfortunately, he never paid Dad any money back.

Uncle Bashir called out loudly to Dad, who was in the back yard brushing up the broken glass from the shed window.

Uncle Bashir once again excitedly shouted, "Ali, come quick and meet your new babi, she is here."

Dad heard his cousin and rushed into the shop. Dad hugged and shook hands with Uncle Bashir. Uncle Bashir was swaying a little, then whilst smiling at Dad he excitedly said, "Look, Ali, I want to introduce you to your new babi, (meaning sister-in-law). Isn't she beautiful? Her name is Shirley."

Dad had that evil angry expression upon his face, and his eyes looked Shirley up and down. He said crossly to his cousin, "Get this Randy out of my shop now." (Randi meaning call girl).

Shirley is a big Scottish woman and is wholly overweight, smelt of alcohol, she was also partially drunk.

Whilst swaying, Shirley looked at Dad as she happily said, "Hello, darling. Firstly, I am no Randy, I am your new babi." (babi meaning sister-in-law)

Dad furiously said to his cousin Bashir, "You know

you are a married man and have six grown up children, now take this drunken woman out of my shop. Have you no respect at all, letting my children see the way you are foolishly behaving?"

Uncle Bashir knew Dad had a very bad temper and quickly took Shirley out of the shop.

He said to Shirley, "Quick get out of the shop, before my cousin gets his big danda out and smashes our heads."

I had never seen Uncle and his girlfriend run out of the shop so quickly, ha ha.

As for me and Ferzana, we kept silent in case Dad picked on us.

March 5th 1972

Mr Singh's son

Jay, is so cute, he is only nine years old and is my regular customer. Whenever Jay came into our shop he would put his hands upon my shop counter and start playing the invisible drums. This became a bit of a habit for Jay and I must say he played very good on the makeshift drum, (meaning my counter), ha ha.

One day Jay came unhappily into the shop and looked at me with a few tears upon his cheeks. It was as if his world had fallen apart. I was truly concerned and asked him, "What's wrong, Jay?"

Jay said, "My father was in such a foul bad mood with my elder brother Gurdip."

I asked Jay what happened.

Jay said gloomily, "You won't believe me, but in front of our mum and dad, my brother got hold of my mother's large, sharp scissors and cut off his long hair. Gurdip knows it is against our Sikh religion to cut our hair. Unfortunately, he disobeyed Dad and our religion."

I was completely shocked, because the Sikh religion forbids cutting of the hair. How could he upset his parents, especially his father who was a high priest in the Sikh temple, plus he had gone against his religion in such a destructive way.

Jay said, "Dad slapped Gurdip on his face so hard that there was a red mark on his cheek. Dad then got hold of his arm and threw him out of the house. My mother tried to help Gurdip but Dad pushed her back into the house."

Later, there was more bad news for Gurdip's parents. Gurdip had been secretly dating for many months. She was a very modern English young lady, and now his girlfriend was pregnant!

Well, whatever you do in the darkness comes out in the light.

Jay said, "My parents had only just found out about Gurdip's antics, now Gurdip had been banished from the house forever."

(That is till Mr Singh calms down) Well, all I can say is I hope all goes fine in Jay's family life.

March 7th 1972

Dad's friend, Hakim

As usual, Dad was very busy cleaning the backyard. At least he had stopped moaning for a while, ha ha! My doting mum was also busy in the back yard, busy watering her babies (meaning her flowers). There were roses, tulips, daffodils and many more beautiful flowers. Sometimes I think Mum loved her flowers more than she did her children.

Whist I was busy stacking the tomato soup tins upon the high shelf behind my counter, suddenly into the shop strolls Uncle Hakim. I said, "As Salaam Valakum, Uncle."

Uncle Hakim smiled and said, "Valakum Salaam beti, where is your dad? I need to speak to him urgently." I told Uncle that Dad was cleaning the leaves which had fallen from next door's tree straight into our backyard, so dad was brushing and shovelling whilst throwing the leaves in our black bin.

I walked into the backyard and told Dad that Uncle Hakim wished to speak to him urgently. Dad came into the kitchen, washed his hands and walked into the shop. Dad and Uncle gave each other a tight hug and Uncle Hakim told Dad that he had a serious problem and whether they could speak privately in the sitting room. Uncle Hakim had tears falling down his red rosy cheeks as he said, "Brother, we are close. We tell each other our problems. Brother, I have a very big problem." Whilst Dad and Uncle Hakim were talking I was listening behind the closed door, was I in for a shock!

Dad told Uncle Hakim to tell him all that had happened, so uncle told him everything. Uncle Hakim put his head down in shame as he sadly said, "Brother, my son Aziz, who is sixteen years old, has been in much trouble. He was casually waiting at the bus stop, then suddenly two tall strong men got hold of Aziz and mugged him. Then Aziz went looking for them and found them going towards Dudley Park, as there was a fun fair on. Then Aziz gathered his friends and told them to meet him at the front gate of Dudley Park. Meanwhile, Aziz had come home, he then looked in the cutlery drawer and took out a long chopper knife. He then put the chopper knife into his large college bag, whilst his friends were all waiting for him near Dudley Park. Upon arriving, Aziz saw the same men who were playing darts, trying to win the prizes, then quickly Aziz ran up to both of the men and hit them both quickly with the large chopper. Aziz and friends quickly ran off towards the park gate, and the next thing that happened was that a few hours later a police van was outside our door then out came three tough policemen who rang the bell and asked for Aziz. Then Aziz came out and the policemen arrested him. The police looked for the chopper in our house but found nothing. Tell me, Brother, what shall I do?"

Hakim was once again crying and fell on Dad's feet to help him.

As usual, Dad gave the wrong advice as he said,

"Hakim, you are in your late sixties and don't need too much stress. If your passport and Aziz's passports are ready then listen carefully to what I am telling you. When your son is given bail, quickly book both your tickets and take him to Pakistan, as you have many relatives and this is the only way out or, I am telling you, your son will be put in a remand centre or worse, sent to prison. The rest is up to you, do not lose your respect!"

Uncle Hakim said in a disheartened voice, "The court case is next week. I will do as you say and we will leave the rest in God's hands."

Sure enough, the court date arrived. Aziz was given bail (Aziz had to sign on at Plat Police Station every day until the court date arrived).

Uncle Hakim phoned Dad and told him the tickets were booked and that they would both be boarding the plane the next day. Dad helped to take Uncle and Aziz to the airport (truly Dad likes to take risks). Uncle thanked Dad for all his help.

When Aziz didn't come to sign on at the police station the police came to his house. Aziz's mother told the police she did not know where Aziz had ran off to, then the police left.

Uncle Hakim was phoning Dad regularly and keeping Dad up to date. The next news was that Uncle Hakim had got Aziz married to his cousin Musarat, and now she is pregnant.

A few months later Aziz, Uncle and Aziz's wife Musarat came back to England. Musarat did not know why he had stayed in Pakistan so long, but she was soon to find out.

Aziz's best friend Jimmy told the police that Aziz had come back home. The police waited and watched from their unmarked car for Aziz to come out of his house. Eventually Aziz took his dad's car to fill the petrol tank at the garage; whilst at the petrol station four policemen rushed out of their car and arrested Aziz.

The court hearing was for the following Monday. Dad was at the court with Uncle Hakim and Dad spoke up for Aziz saying he had mental health problems and was on medication in Pakistan. Aziz had told doctors he was hearing voices to tell him to harm people, and he had to obey the spirits. Aziz was sent to an asylum due to his mental state.

Aziz had been in the asylum for five months and unfortunately, he was behaving like the other patients there. Uncle Aziz told Dad everything and about Aziz's ill health.

Uncle Hakim cried whilst saying, "Brother, I thought all would be alright. Apparently, all turned out bad. Aziz has been put on much medication, and now has mental health problems. He has put on so much weight. I should not have taken him to Pakistan and just let him be put in prison for a while, Brother. It was a mistake but God is the bigger planner." Then Uncle Hakim sadly went on his way home.

Well, Dad you have given the wrong advice again! What can I say! Dad should stay out of people's problems or he will soon have more problems himself.

March 10th 1972

Eddie, our adopted grandad

Many weeks had passed and our business was booming. We had never been so busy; it was hard work and the hours were very long but we made it. Each day new customers would be arriving and thanking us for opening so late. Our shop was the first to open on a Sunday, and there would be customers queuing outside our shop wow! I could not believe our luck, money was rolling in.

One Sunday an elderly gentleman came into our shop to buy some bread. He was so jolly and very polite and spoke with a strong Irish accent.

He smiled and said, "Hello, dear, my name is Eddie Wood it is nice to meet you."

Well! Here we go a new beginning for us, in came our adopted granddad.

Eddie would come into our shop regularly. He would talk about the past and how life was a struggle and he would go on and on – how interesting and sort of boring. The only downfall Eddie had was that he would put snuff up his nose every hour and the snuff would leave marks on his clothing and on our new carpet in the lounge. Guess who had to hoover up each evening after Eddie had gone home? Yes! It was me. Eddie had his good points – he was a great listener, and he was never judgemental. Everyone in our family would tell him all their problems; he was like the family councillor. Eddie had won our hearts and our respect.

On one occasion, Eddie had come to visit and we were all talking to him for hours. Eddie was getting tired and politely said, "It's getting late" but Ferzana and Miriam nervously asked Eddie to stay a little longer as Dad was in such a temper. Dad was waiting for Aftab to come home. It was getting so late, ten thirty at night to be precise.

Dad had his danda ready to hit Aftab with (it's a pity child protection people were not around at that time).

Another twenty minutes had passed and my dad was getting very worried. Then suddenly, without warning, Aftab appeared at the top of the stairs. Aftab confidently said, "Dad, what's up? Why have you got that stick in your hand?" Dad swore at Aftab and asked him where he had been. Aftab said, "Dad, I have been in my bedroom doing my homework which has to be handed in tomorrow! My important exams are coming up soon."

The truth being he had climbed up the drainpipe onto the small shop roof and then climbed into Miriam's bedroom and then sneaked into the attic (that was where his bedroom was). Clever lad. Thank God Dad had calmed down.

Poor Eddie felt so tired he had to go as it was past his bedtime. My dad came with me in the car to drop Eddie off at home. All I can say is that it had been a nerve-racking, traumatic night.

March 13th 1972

Hurray, it's Mother's Day

Here it comes again, sweet wonderful Mother's Day. What did my mother like to receive every year on Mother's Day? There is no way anybody could have ever guessed! One present was a blue box of snuff, the more the merrier, followed by a long fat cigar. Mother was not like many other people who would put snuff up their nose. Mother would get her little finger, put a little bit of brown snuff on it, then off it merrily went into her mouth upon her bottom lip, then she closed her mouth. Yes, Mother was in heaven!

This was an addiction, but no matter, the snuff would calm our mother down. After all, she had been taking the snuff in her mouth from the tender age of fifteen.

Each year on Mother's Day, I was the one who made the meal for Mother, which she really appreciated. Mum did not like too much chilli in her curry. The meal took a while to prepare but Mother was worth her weight in gold. First course was samosas and pakoras, a mild prawn curry, lamb korma curry with chapattis and rice and peas. As for dessert, semolina pudding, yummy.

Ferzana and Miriam wrapped up the Mother's Day presents, which contained a box of Dairy Milk chocolates (which Mother ended up giving to all her children), a nice cotton blue sequined cardigan, a bunch of red roses and that damn box of snuff. The last present was her long fat cigar. Mum did not smoke / inhale the cigar but she would put it in her mouth, then blow the smoke in the corners of our shop and the living room, which Mother said would take the black magic and evil eye off. Oh, how unusual.

Mother's lips would quiver waiting for her large box of snuff, which had twelve little boxes of snuff inside. That positively made her Mother's Day. Mother was given a kiss from all her doting children. She had wholeheartedly appreciated all we had done for her. There is no way we could ever repay our mother for the pain and hard work she had gone through to raise all her children. Love you, Mother. Happy Mother's Day, we all love you.

A POEM WRITTEN FOR MY MOTHER ON MOTHER'S DAY

A loving, caring Mother is hard to find
You are humble, affectionate and extremely kind
You are one in a million, you're such a compassionate
  mother
An angel in disguise, there can be no other

You love us, you nurture us and protect us all the time
Praying to the angels for this MOTHER of mine
Your eyes are caring, you have a sweet loving smile
It's Mother's Day, come rest for a while

Just wish to tell you, that we all love you
You Are the Best Mother in the World
No other person could replace you
Just wish to say WE ALL LOVE YOU

March 15th 1972

Janet lost her mother

Janet is such a caring beautiful friend of mine. She is of similar age, but today when she came into the shop she had tears flowing down her saddened face.

I was concerned and asked her, "What's wrong, are you alright?"

Janet could hardly speak, choking back her heart-breaking tears she said, "My mother died in hospital yesterday. I cannot come to terms with it." She then cried uncontrollably.

I quickly walked up to her and consoled her by putting my warm comforting arms around her shoulder, whilst tears were also flowing down my disbelieving eyes. I inquisitively asked Janet what had happened. Janet told me that her mother had terminal cancer for many years and she had been very ill, plus she was suffering from aches and pains and was on so much medication that she was sick most of the time.

Janet looked up at me as she said, "You don't know what's it like going back to an empty house. It's scary, as well as lonely." Janet put her head down whilst tears fell down her swollen face. She pushed back the tears and said, "Mother will be buried at eleven o'clock this Thursday at Southern Cemetery. If you can come to support me, please do."

I told Janet I would come to pay my respect and if she

needed any help I would always be here for her; my door was always open for her.

Janet had a glaze in her eyes as though she was in a dream. She looked at me then nodded and went unhappily on her way.

I felt blessed that my mother was still alive, this was an eye-opener for me. Now I appreciated my mother even more, GOD bless her.

March 18th 1972

Dad physically assaulted the milkman

Dad had the winter blues. He was feeling rather gloomy, but that did not stop him from moaning at everyone, including my mother. We all tried to somehow stay out of his way. What happened next was shocking as well as very distressing.

I was happily humming, whilst filling the stock in the shop. Dad caught a glimpse of the milkman from the corner of his eye. He was fixing his hair before entering the shop, then our jolly milkman, John, entered the shop, licking his big lips as saliva trickled slowly down the side of his hungry mouth. John is a short, obese man with long ginger hair – best described as a human version of a ginger bull dog. He was carrying a crate of milk, eggs and orange juice.

John is a very talkative man. He had a habit of putting his tongue out and moving it left to right, ugh! He always liked to have a chat with the girls in the shop, (which Dad disliked) but he mostly talked to me.

This time, Dad was peeping from the small window inside the adjoining door. Dad came irritably into the shop and told John, "You have delivered the milk and groceries, now go."

John started laughing at Dad (big mistake!). John said to Dad, "Can I go out with your beautiful daughter Malika? I really fancy her." Once again, Dad asked John politely to get out of the shop. John did not listen and ignored Dad. I could see Dad's hand's itching (big mistake) whilst John still went on talking to me. Dad was fuming then, without warning, from behind the shop door Dad got hold of his danda then, for the last time, Dad repeated to John to get out of the shop, and once again, John ignored Dad! So, Dad lifted his heavy danda and hit John over the head with it. Suddenly, blood started squirting from John's head wound. John collapsed upon the cold tiled floor but he managed to get himself up and he ran bleeding profusely out of the shop door.

Meanwhile, my mother, Aftab and my dopy sister Miriam had come back from the chemist. They told Dad that our milkman was running down the road whilst blood was pouring from his head onto his clothes. Dad knew that John must have phoned the police, so he told us all to tell the police that John had tried to molest Malika, and that dad had to protect his daughter from this fiend of a milkman. All I was thinking was, Dad, why do you keep getting yourself into a mess all the time and causing us all problems? Sure enough, three policemen came and arrested Dad, then they put him in the back of the police van. Dad was driven to the police station for questioning. I also had to go to the police station to give a statement.

Unfortunately, I had to give a false statement.

John said sorry to my dad (poor man) and he never stepped into our shop again.

Well, sure enough, we had been allocated a new milkman and he had better watch out as well!

Dad should learn to calm himself down in some situations – he is such a bad tempered stubborn man.

One day he will get himself into so much trouble and God forbid may not be able to get himself out of any problems.

As for Dad's danda, it waits patiently in the usual place behind the fridge for anyone who dares to cross the line while Dad's around.

March 24th 1972

Getting bored of the shop

My dream of becoming a shop keeper had soon worn off. I just wanted to do some work which was less boring, plus I just wished to earn my own money. (Working in this prison shop I was earning nil!)

I could take as much money as I wished from the shop till, but I somehow felt guilty.

I told Dad that I was bored and I wanted to find a job. At first Dad was not happy that I had intended to look for a job, but soon he said, "It's up to you. Do what you think is right."

I applied for a job as a typist at a firm called Direct, and guess what? I got the job. I felt like flying as I had never worked outside my dad's shop before.

I was told to start work on the following Monday.

Monday morning soon arrived, my clothes were immaculate and my hair was tied back with a silver patterned clip, my make-up was stunning, then off I casually went to start my new job as a typist.

Arriving at my destination, I opened the tall wide old oak door, and upon entering there was a long winding corridor, but I soon found the door with the sign 'Sales'. I calmly entered the office, still feeling confident. There were eight people working there and they all greeted me. I shyly said "Good morning". Most of the staff wished me good morning as well.

I had been given a lot of work to type out. My fingers were hurting and my legs felt numb, but I was so happy at being given this job opportunity.

When I arrived home my family asked how my day had been. All I could say was it was tiring.

I rested for a couple of hours then worked in the shop for a few hours.

Next morning, I was off to work again, but something had changed. Someone else was sat at my desk and in my seat doing the typing. The clerk on the other desk asked me to make everyone some tea and everyone had me running around doing errands for them. My heart sank. I was hired as an invoice typist and was running around like a servant for everyone in the office.

I thought, *right that's it.* I got my bag and walked out. I then ran all the way home in tears. My immaculate make up had melted all over my face and I felt like a sorrowful clown!

Dad was smoking outside the shop and I told him what had happened. Dad lovingly hugged me, which made me cry even more. Dad said, "This is your own shop, it is your business, you are your own boss and no one can tell you what to do. You were the one who wanted to find a job." I hugged Dad back and walked happily into the shop. I then took my rightful place once again behind the shop counter.

Truly, you don't realise what you have till it's gone. I was lucky to get my shop and my pride back.

March 29ᵗʰ 1972

The cream

A special visitor is coming to visit us from Pakistan, it was our elderly Aunty Hameeda. She was the head of the family and highly respected by all, especially my dad.

Dad told me to drive to the airport. When we reached the airport, we looked for Arrivals, sure enough Aunty Hameeda was waiting patiently outside. Dad hugged Aunty and then picked up her heavy suitcase and put it in the large blue family saloon car.

We arrived home with Aunty Hameeda and all her heavy, bulky luggage.

Aunty Hameeda was given my clean comfortable room for her one month holiday.

She was very strict but had lovely green cat eyes, and was so light-skinned that she would have passed as an English woman, if it wasn't for her accent.

She walked with a brown walking stick, and upon the top the walking stick was a golden duck handle.

Aunty Hameeda had bought us all lovely presents from Pakistan: silver and golden high heel shoes, ornaments, (including a marble Taj Mahal) incense sticks, black leather modern bags, Tavees (small square necklaces) to take the evil eye of people and much more.

Miriam, my younger sister, came back from school and saw Auntie Hameeda

She respectively said, "As Salaam Alaykum."

Aunty replied back, "Walekum Salaam."

Miriam could not help looking at Aunty Hameeda because she was so fair-skinned.

Miriam dreamed of being lighter skinned and beautiful, she then rushed upstairs to get ready.

Miriam is such a nosy child. She sneaked into Aunty's bedroom to see which cream Aunty was using to lighten her face. On the dressing table she saw a long white tube of cream, just near Aunty's fancy golden comb, pale powder and pink lipstick.

Miriam thought to herself *This is the cream Aunty uses as a skin lightener*, so she carefully and quietly opened the cap of the cream and put some cream in her hands. Then she rubbed cream all over her face. She was feeling confident that she was getting lighter skinned and beautiful, well that's what she thought.

Miriam quickly ran downstairs so no one would notice that she had been missing. She sat happily next to Aunty Hameeda.

Miriam looked excitedly at Aunty, whilst Aunty stared back at her.

Suddenly Aunty Hameeda said, "Miriam, I can smell something like antiseptic cream or some strong smell on you." Then all of a sudden Miriam felt her face tingling.

Mum asked Miriam what was wrong. She told Mum that she had used Aunty's face cream on her face, which was on the dressing table. It was a long white tube and her face was now burning.

Aunty Hameeda scolded Miriam and told her that was not face cream, but it was her rheumatism cream for the severe pains in her legs.

Miriam panicked and started to cry, she quickly ran up to the bathroom and washed her face. By now her face looked like a bright red strawberry, and there were a few sore spots appearing. All Miriam could hear downstairs was giggling and laughter.

Aunty Hameeda was laughing the most – she could not believe that Miriam had actually used her rheumatism cream on her face.

It took Miriam a few days to get over the shock of her face becoming red and sore, but at least for the first time she had heard Aunty Hameeda laugh, and guess what? Miriam became Aunty's favourite niece.

Aunty Hameeda decided to come along with us to the cash and carry, and enjoyed walking around with the help of her strong wooden walking stick. Aunty saw alcohol and turned her face away, disgusted, saying, "Tobah, Tobah" (Penance, Penance), then passing the meat counters she was shocked seeing pork and pig heads also some other undesirable meat, fatty lamb chops, mincemeat and much more. Once again, Aunty was stressing and shouting in temper, "Tobah Tobah Tobah".

We were at the cash and carry for over an hour and all Aunty would do most of the time was moan. Aunty angrily said, "I will never come to this big, foul unclean cash and carry again"

I told Aunty politely, "This is a cash and carry where all shop keepers come to buy their stock."

We soon left the cash and carry (Aunty had found this place very undesirable).

Dad and Aunty are so alike, they both have bad tempers and can moan for England.

Only one more week left before Aunty goes back to Pakistan so until then, we have to all be on our best behaviour (if that was possible).

As for Dad, he was just like an angel. He never moaned, shouted or said a wrong word, because Aunty Hameeda was like his elder sister, and she would have slapped him if he was out of order. Thank God for Aunty Hameeda – she is the only one-person Dad is petrified of.

April 5th 1972

Drunken Cathy

A new customer arrived in our neighbourhood, her name was Cathy and she had arrived from Scotland. She was such a jolly, chubby lady, but her downfall was her drinking as she loved her whisky and rum. Whenever she came into the shop she smelled of alcohol, phew!

But she was a happy regular paying customer.

When Cathy came into our shop for a third time I introduced her to Mum, all I could say is that my mum had definitely taken a liking to Cathy.

Whenever Cathy came into the shop, she would be a little drunk and whilst laughing, would yell, "Malika, where is Mamma, I got a box of chocolates for her. Oh, there is Mamma. Hi Mamma, just look what I have bought for you. My husband Jim works at the chocolate factory and gets lots of chocolates at reduced prices. I have bought you a couple of large chocolate bars and a couple of Fruit and Nut chocolates bars."

I don't know about fruit and nut, but Cathy was a bit nutty and fruity, but she was such a warm, kind-hearted caring woman.

Cathy has two young children, Susan and Mike, they are both well-mannered, polite and caring, just like their mother.

Cathy had been living in the area for about five months, and one day she told me she had been caring for an elderly lady named Jane, who lived across the road.

Jane was so grateful for the help and company that Cathy had given her, that she kindly gave Cathy a couple of antique jugs.

Jane's son, who frequently visited his mother, thanked Cathy for all the hard work she put in to help his mother. He was so grateful that as a thank you gesture he gave Cathy eighty pounds and two more antique pots –by the way, each pot was worth two hundred pounds.

Cathy happily said, "Malika, guess what, Jane's son, who is such a lovely man gave me a vast amount of money and more antiques. I must tell Mamma, where is Mamma? Are you hiding from me, Mamma? Where are you? Ha ha."

Mum was in the back yard pretending to put the washing out. Cathy came up to Mamma and gave her a big kiss and a warm hug, whilst breathing heavily upon her face with her strong alcoholic breath. Mum had to use her salbutamol asthma inhaler spray, wonder why! Ha ha

April 12th 1972

My dog Jason saw a ghost

Me and Jason

My large, Alsatian dog named Jason is an ex guard dog. He is a tough and faithful beast, and he was afraid of no one, except Dad. I think everyone was afraid of Dad!

One evening I could hear Jason barking, and loudly growling in the kitchen, I went to check, the poor

94

thing was terrified of something, seeing him like that scared me

I tried to calm Jason down and get him to eat some of his favourite meaty dog biscuits, but Jason's eyes were fixed on a special spot. He may have seen something; he was adamant and he did not move.

Jason looked above and his eyes were secured on something or someone, then it struck me that he must be observing a ghost or something more sinister.

Dad and Mum had gone to Auntie Zena's house to express their condolences at the death of her mother.

Frightened at being left all alone in the shop, with one mad dog, I phoned my dad and told him I was a little nervous and frightened and whether he could he please come back to the shop quickly as Jason was acting most unusual.

Returning to the eerie kitchen, I saw what was making Jason go berserk. My eyes looked towards the top of the shelf on the wall and there was Ferzana's new blonde curly wig, which was placed on a white frightening statuette head.

Jason was still whimpering as he had never seen a wig or statuette head before. To Jason it must have looked like a head without a body! I just couldn't stop laughing and when my family came home they couldn't stop giggling.

As for poor Jason, he must have had nightmares for weeks!

April 16th 1972

Lazy Miriam

Well, the school holidays have arrived – one week off for Miriam she can help us all in the shop.

Monday morning and Dad was busy stacking the shelves with all the tins of soup, there was vegetable soup, tomato soup and much more.

Miriam came nosing into the shop, with her little shopping bag to get her delicious snacks including chocolates, sweets, crisps and cake. Dad looked at her and said sarcastically, "Miriam, that's a lot of junk food, 10 girls could eat that, have your friends come around? If your friends have not come my little chubby daughter then I would appreciate it if you would help me with the stock and put the tins on the shelf."

Miriam looked at Dad moodily but she had to help him. She had no choice. After thirty minutes Miriam complained, "Dad, I hope you don't expect me to help you in the shop too often as I have lots of homework to do, plus I have to help Mum in the kitchen." Dad looked sternly at Miriam and angrily shouted, "Since when have you ever helped your mother in the kitchen, so don't lie to me as all day you are watching bloody television, and not once have I seen you doing your homework. I am your father, do not lie to me."

Then Dad slammed the rest of the tins upon the shelf and mumbled to himself. Miriam truly knew how to wind Dad up. Dad looked at Miriam and saw tears trickling down her little chubby face, then Miriam looked at Dad and he got hold of her and picked her up saying, "Miriam, you are my baby. Please don't cry, you know you are my favourite child. Wipe your tears, Daddy loves you so much. I cannot bear to see any tears falling from your eyes. Here is a big bar of chocolate and here is five pounds. Go with your mother and get a nice dress." Miriam knew how to soften Dad's heart, what can I say?

Miriam decided to get some fresh air. She opened the shop door and saw Mrs. Singh stood near her gate, so Miriam walked up to Mrs. Singh and said in a jolly voice, "Hello, Mrs. Singh how are you?"

Mrs. Singh smiled as she said, "I am fine." Miriam wondered what should she say next Miriam smiled and casually said, "Last week Mum and I went to watch an Asian film. It was really good, it was called *Dhulan*, and in the end the woman's husband died, then the woman broke her glass bangles on the nearby wall. Why do the women break their bangles?"

Mrs. Singh was getting annoyed with Miriam asking her these nasty questions, and shouted, "Miriam, get away from my gate. You're wishing bad luck upon me talking about what breaking of the bangles means, go away now."

Mrs. Singh was so upset she slammed her front door behind her.

Miriam told Dad what had happened and Dad sternly said, "Miriam, you should never mention about Asian women breaking their glass bangles when their husband dies. It is definitely bad luck, now go and help your sister put the chocolates on the shelves."

I cannot wait till the week holiday finishes and

Miriam is back at school, then she can give her teachers headache.

Well, Miriam has still not learnt her lesson, the spoilt brat, ha ha

April 20th 1972

Mrs O'Connor died

Mrs O'Connor was a very dignified woman, she was tall, had long grey hair which she wrapped into a neat pony tail. She was slim and attractive considering her age, and she spoke with a strong Irish accent.

Mrs O'Connor always came into the shop for a long chat. The reason being, she was always left alone at home, whilst her builder husband Ian went out to work from morning till late evening.

Mrs O'Connor did not pay cash, she always took credit from our shop. Her groceries included bread, milk cheese and bacon; she would always pay us the money for her goods at the end of each week. The rest of her shopping was bought from the large supermarket up the road (this seriously annoyed Dad).

Every Friday afternoon my jealous Dad would peep through the shop window, so he could see Mrs O'Connor taking her three heavy bags of shopping home – all these goods she had bought from the local Ebro supermarket.

Dad had started to notice Mrs O'Connor had not been in the shop for eight days and wondered why. He thought she may have found another shop that gave her credit.

Dad knew she owed us money for the previous bill.

John, who was a regular jolly customer, is short and chubby with no teeth in his mouth. John suffers from severe arthritis. John always had a smile on his face whenever he came into the shop. He was a man who knew everyone's business and gossip. He told Dad that Mrs O'Connor, who lived down the road, had died over a week ago. She had been ill in hospital and had died. Dad was so upset, mostly because she never paid off her bill before dying.

A week later Dad saw Mrs O' Connor's husband, Ian who was across the road taking his pet Alsatian dog for a walk. Dad called John over and said, "I am very sorry to hear about your dear wife's death, and oh, by the way your wife always took credit from me, and she had not paid her food bill."

Mr O'Connor asked Dad how much his deceased wife had owed him. Dad said, "The bill was only five pounds."

Mr O'Connor sank his hands deep into his pocket and pulled out a five-pound note. He sadly said, "Here is the money my wife owes you," then Mr O'Connor put his head down and went gloomily on his way.

Oh, Dad how could you ask Mr O'Connor for the money his deceased wife owed you before dying, but come to think of it, anything is possible with my dad. Sometimes I think Dad has no heart or conscience. Well, that's my dad for you. You either like Dad or hate him.

April 28th 1972

Feeling unwell

Today it was a very chilly, cold day and I was feeling rather unwell. I was coughing and sneezing and I had a severe headache. Dad made me look after the shop, as he must have thought I was faking being ill just so I could go into the living room to have a rest. Dad is a slave driver – he should get a life!

It was five o'clock in the evening, when in walked Dad's friend Uncle Shah.
    I said, "Salaam Uncle Shah."

Uncle said happily, "Hello, Malika. You have a very bad cold and should be resting. Where is your dad?"

I called out for Dad to come quickly into the shop, as Uncle Shah was waiting for him. Dad rushed into the shop and hugged him tight, Dad asked Uncle Shah where he had been for the past few weeks. Uncle Shah winked saying, "You know, Ali, I had to go to get the illegal items off the ship, which had landed at Liverpool docks. Ali, there is so much stock which includes, for example, fashionable Indian clothes and shoes, going cheap, but the main thing I went to buy was the drugs which were going at a reasonable price on the ship. I make good profit from these goods. The druggies rush to me as I sell the drugs cheap – that is how I bought my detached house, through the drug money. Yes! That is the life."

I gave Dad a dirty look – how could he associate with

people like Uncle Shah. Even the mention of the word drugs made my skin crawl, ugh!

Uncle Shah said sympathetically to Dad, "Ali, your daughter looks ill why don't you let her rest?"

Dad looked at me and said to Uncle, "Malika is alright. I have put the electric heater on behind the shop counter, so there is no worry. She is warm there. Never mind Malika, you come into the sitting room. Malika, you have to stay and look after the shop."

I looked angrily at Dad and said, "Yes, Dad, I am alright. You go and have a good chat with Uncle Shah." In my heart I was cursing Dad, he had no feelings at all for anyone.

Well! You either like dad or you hate him. I know in my heart that I hated him today.

May 1st 1972

Ferzana reluctantly teaches Dad to drive

Ferzana had recently passed her driving test and dad was so proud of her – the reason being he thought she would teach him to improve his driving skills!

Believe me, I had tried on numerous occasions to try and teach Dad to drive, but unfortunately, on Dad's first driving lesson, I nearly ended up having a nervous breakdown. The shock took me over two weeks to fully recover.

Dad politely said to Ferzana, "Come on my daughter, please teach me to drive, put the learner driver plates on the van, and then we can go for driving lessons."
Ferzana was not happy at all to give Dad driving lessons; as she had seen the severe impact it had on her younger sister (me).

Dad then spoke angrily to Ferzana who refused to give dad any driving lessons (big mistake).
Dad yelled and cursed at Ferzana; the poor girl had tears rolling down her rosy red cheeks.
Ferzana shook fearfully. Dad seemed to have that effect on everyone he knew!

Ferzana had no choice but to obey dad and put the learner plates on the van – God help her!

Dad sat on the driving seat with his hands upon the steering wheel. He politely told Ferzana to sit on the front passenger seat beside him whilst he drove, and

Ferzana reluctantly had to do as she was told. Dad felt confident and in control sitting behind the wheel, Dad happily said, "Here we go, Ferzana. Don't worry, your dad is with you, nothing will happen. If something happens, we will die together. You know I am improving my driving techniques every day."

Dad drove slowly, whilst jerking down the road at five miles per hour. He drove towards the Chorlton leisure centre. The car coughed, choked and stalled, and by this time Ferzana was getting very worried. She had a panic attack and started to turn pale (wonder why)?

Dad impatiently said, "I told you I could drive. Please just keep calm and leave everything to God and me." The way dad drove, he could lead her up to God?

Dad finally reached Chorlton, then he suddenly pressed the emergency brakes near the traffic lights (which obviously by now had turned red). Ferzana's heart started to palpitate – she was having another panic attack. She opened the car door and got out. She quickly started to walk back towards home. Dad called Ferzana to get back into the car, but Ferzana would not listen, she did not want to die in the car with Dad.

Would you believe it, Dad slowly turned the van around in the middle of the busy main road, whilst many car drivers pressed their horns angrily at him, Dads reaction was to rudely stick up two fingers back at them.

Dad tried driving back to the shop, but regrettably, on the way he stalled about twenty times. He was just five minutes away from the shop when a large police van with its sirens blaring stopped in front of Dad. then Dad put his emergency brake on, the policeman got out of his van and asked Dad to get out of his vehicle, then the policeman asked to see Dad's driving license (big shame). Dad told the policeman the truth – that he had a provisional driver license. The policeman took all the details down in his little black notebook then dad was told to take the required documents to the nearest police station and to leave the car at the side of the road.

Dad walked irritably back to the shop. He was very angry especially with Ferzana for deserting him. When Dad eventually reached the shop, Ferzana was busy serving a few customers so she had luck on her side. Dad went upstairs and just snoozed his depression off.

As for Ferzana, she couldn't care less. She just thanked God she did not have to give Dad any more driving lessons.

Dad had to go to court and he was fined fifty pounds, as well as having four points put on his driving license. Dad, for God's sake, please, just give up learning to drive, or you're going to drive your children insane!

May 4th 1972

Quiet day

Such a beautiful morning, the sun is blasting its way into the shop window, the birds are merrily singing, the butterflies fluttering to and fro, I just want to sing merrily la la la la la. Must be going mad in my young age ha ha. I think I spoke too soon as into the shop strolls a young couple of lovebirds. The man looked more like a hippy; he was a bit scruffy, he had long tangled plaited hair up to his shoulders. He was carrying a small guitar in his left hand, he looked in his early thirties, and was accompanied by his, what I presumed to be his young girlfriend. They walked happily hand in hand. She looked like a modern teenager, with long blonde curly hair down to her shoulders. She wore a long black and white spotted dress down to her ankles. On her eyes, she had thick black make-up and upon her lips she wore blood red bright lipstick, ugh!

The man asked me for a long Mason cigar and a small box of matches. As for his girlfriend, she picked some chocolates, consisting of two Mars bars, one Bounty and two Avro candy sticks. After he paid me for his shopping, he looked at me, blew me a kiss and winked lovingly.

Then, all of a sudden, his girlfriend slapped him so hard across the left side of his cheek (which turned a bright red colour).

Her body was shaking, her eyes were bulging, she screamed and hissed loudly and angrily she said, "It will take more than bloody chocolates to calm me down, you two timing piece of shit! You had an affair behind my back in the past and you expect me to forgive you so quickly. You even blew a kiss to the shop assistant. We have been together for one year and this this how you treat someone that you love. Well, you can piss off now as I am going to leave you. I can't take this pressure of knowing that you have betrayed me." Then she cried hysterically.

Her boyfriend calmly, whilst shaking, said, "Look, you are carrying our baby, please be calm. I'm sorry, I just wish I could turn the clock back but cannot. You know I love you very much. Look, I am falling on my knees please, I beg you, marry me. I am serious, please say yes." The young woman wiped away her heart-breaking tears and hugged her boyfriend and nodded, which I presumed meant yes!

I was watching in amazement. I was shocked. It felt like I was in a dream. The man grabbed his girlfriend by the waist and started to cry and apologise to her. They hugged each other.

With all this drama going on, I felt like this was better than *Coronation Street*. The couple thanked me and went on their way, and I was flabbergasted. Oh my God, I just wish them the best of luck. Well, that's gossip to tell Mum and Dad.

May 6th 1972

The rats

Dad had gone abroad to Lahore, in Pakistan for a few weeks, because his elder brother Hakim was not too well, so I was left to take control of the shop.

Mum was never the moody type, but for some reason she kept shouting and moaning at me. I wondered if it may be the menopause making Mum have these mood swings. Or could Mum be thinking that Dad may marry a younger woman in Pakistan.

There was only so much I could take! I was in such a rage, that I quickly put on my coat and walked out of the shop whilst thinking to myself *to hell with the shop.*

Tears were rolling down my face. I quickly took a clean tissue out of my pocket and wiped away my tears. I carried on walking down the road, and then caught the number eighty-five bus towards town, then I went to the Regal Cinema to see if there was a nice horror movie on. I looked down the list of films and I thought *this film looks rather interesting.* It was simply called *The Rats*, a nice horror film (how wrong could I have been). I bought a ticket, and some sweet popcorn, plus an ice-cold cola drink.

I waited anxiously for the film to start. I looked around and noticed there were not many people that had come to watch this film, except for some elderly men (*funny*, I thought). I calmed my temper and relaxed myself, as the film was about to start.

The film started and I was so excited at the thought of becoming frightened. What I saw made me sink back into my seat – this was not a horror film, it was a dirty X-rated film. I was in utter shock as I quickly got up from my seat, put my head down and ran out of the cinema, I thought phew! Thank God, my family were not here with me, hopefully I pray they would never find out about the shameful situation I was in.

This embarrassing and great shock soon calmed my foul temper down. On returning home, Mum was panicking and upset. She thought I had left home (never). I hugged my mum and made up with her. Would I ever leave my mum? Hell, no. My mum is my life and my everything, or on second thoughts? Ha ha, you never know.

May 8ᵗʰ 1972

Bertha and Martha

Today was such a cold, windy and dismal day. Dad had removed my one bar electric heater, which I had kept behind the shop counter to keep myself warm. Instead, he replaced the heater with a paraffin heater. (I am sure, by law, that a paraffin heater should not be kept anywhere near food or on shop premises.) Well, what does that tell you about my dad?

Well, it's one o'clock in the afternoon. Mum had fetched my well-deserved lunch into the shop for me to eat (yes, I even eat my meals in the shop, ha ha). The lunch consisted of a cheese and onion sandwich, one packet of cheese and onion crisps, a small chocolate cake and last but not least, a can of lemonade. Yummy. I quickly gobbled the food down and gently cleaned my lips with a clean tissue. I truly enjoyed that lunch.

I gazed out of my shop window wishing my Prince Charming would enter the shop and carry me off, but it's back to reality.

From afar I noticed Bertha and Martha (they are twins and are disabled pensioners). They were strolling towards my shop. My first thought was shall I hide and let Dad serve them, or should I pluck up the courage and serve them myself? The guilt got the better of me. Yes, I stayed, mentally preparing myself.

Bertha and Martha are our very good, reliable customers. The only problem is when they depart from the shop, they leave me utterly and mentally drained, bless them. Here come the sisters, one by one! Into the shop walks Bertha (she is the one with dark brown hair) and Martha has blonde hair.

Bertha smiled whilst saying, "Hello, Malika, how are you? Well I hope."

I calmly said, "I am very well, thank you."

Martha starts to grin as she spontaneously said, "Yes! How are you?"

Whilst looking at Martha in the eyes I said, "I am alright, thanks."

Bertha hastily said, "Malika, can I have two tins of Hiller Beans, one large white sliced bread, one Burton butter, two boxes of Joy orange juice, one packet of royal sugar, one large bottle of milk, one dozen eggs, and that's it, thanks."

Martha looked me up and down and started to repeat what her sister Bertha had ordered.

"Malika, so that's beans, bread, butter, juice, sugar, eggs and milk, thanks," said Martha, grinning.

Bertha excitedly said, "Oh, I do like your cake display. The cakes look scrumptious – chocolate cakes, cream cakes lemon custard cakes, yummy."

Martha licked her lips as she said, "Oh! What lovely cakes. Such a selection."

Truly, the sisters had a habit of repeating each other's sentence. Bertha paid me for their goods, but before the twins left they asked the usual questions.

Martha asked me if I had a boyfriend yet. She calmly said, "You are a beautiful, stunning, caring young lady. Any young man would fall instantly in love with you."

Bertha looked at me as to what to say next. She looked me straight in my eyes whilst saying, "Malika, you are blessed you are a very pretty woman. Any male would fall in love with you."

Bertha asked me if I liked the colours purple and black, and Martha asked me if I liked the colours maroon and ebony (the colours are the same but different names, ahhhh). The bloody repeating went on for ten minutes. I had a severe headache, they were making me have a panic attack. I thought I would go insane.

Finally, the mad twins picked up their shopping bags, then they waved at me whilst shouting, "Bye bye, Malika, see you on Saturday." Then they closed the shop door gently behind them.

As soon as Bertha and Martha had left the shop, I gasped a sigh of relief. The next time the elderly twins enter this shop, Dad will have to serve the both of them (two in one). I don't want to end up having a nervous breakdown at such a young and tender age.

May 12th 1972

Ferzana worked at the surgery

Ferzana decided to take a part-time job in the evening, to finance her expensive lifestyle. Aftab (the poor lad), besides having homework, also helped us out in the shop. Well, actually Dad forced Aftab to work in the shop in the evening.

Ferzana started work near home, at the "Doctor Khan Medical Centre" on Charlton Road. Ferzana had been working for two months at the doctor's surgery. She loved her job – the reason being she had a lot of responsibility and authority (I personally think she was happy to be away from this Prison Shop).

Whenever Ferzana came home from work she would always talk about Dr Khan.
    Ferzana worked for Dr Khan, a tall, handsome and very polite person. After work, he would always drop Ferzana off at the shop in his expensive high-class silver Jaguar car.

Lately, Mum and I had noticed Ferzana had been coming home later and later.

One morning I angrily said to Ferzana, "What is the reason you keep coming home late every night. There cannot be that much overtime."

Ferzana put her head down in shame, she had that look of guilt upon her face. She just kept silent.

The following evening, whilst Ferzana was at work, I went upstairs to her bedroom and looked in her wardrobe to see if there was any proof of an affair. There, hidden amongst her neatly folded coloured cardigans, I found what I had much suspicion of. When Ferzana came home from work, I called her upstairs to her bedroom (which she shared with Miriam). I asked her who had given her all these expensive perfumes and make-up sets, as her wages could never pay for all these expensive items. I then showed her some tiny pills and asked her what they were for. Ferzana's reaction was to cry hysterically. I then knew by her sorrowful tears that Doctor Khan had been taking advantage of my elder sister. He had been prescribing contraceptive pills and the pills were to be taken orally to stop my sister getting pregnant. If Dad had found out in rage he would have killed Ferzana, along with the pervert Doctor Khan.

I told Ferzana that there was no way she was going back to work, and that I would be having a stern talk with Doctor Khan. Ferzana had known that Doctor Khan was married and had two young children. Impatiently, I said to her, "Have you no conscience at all? Just because he is a doctor you should have some self- respect. Why have you had an affair with that dirty trash of a doctor?"

Early in the morning I phoned Doctor Khan I told him he was very lucky that I had not reported him to his seniors or the higher authority. I told him he should be ashamed of having taken advantage of a naive girl, and said, "God help you when I see your wife," and then I slammed the phone down. I told Ferzana to tell

Dad that she had got bored of the job.

As for Doctor Khan, the last I heard of him was that the police had arrested him for molesting and groping many of his teenage patients. It was about time that he was caught, the creepy rat deserved what he got! He was sent to prison for three years. I pity his wife and children, it was not their fault.

Well now Ferzana, you were saved, but many were not saved from that pervert doctor. I calmly said, "Ferzana, I have not told Dad about your obscene behaviour, and how degrading and disrespectful you have been, bringing dishonour on your family. Now Ferzana, you can take your duty with me at Ali's Desi Shop. Any other perverts better beware of Dad's Desi danda."

May 18th 1972

A lady we called Cookoo

Today is such a cold, windy, rainy day. I was feeling so bored and tired. I thought I would have a nosy to see what my younger brother Aftab was doing in the attic. I asked Mum to keep an eye on the shop whilst I spied on Aftab, because I wanted to see if he had finished his homework. I tiptoed quietly whilst climbing the winding stairway to his small bedroom in the attic.

I noticed Aftab's door was partially open – he would usually lock his bedroom door for his own privacy whilst doing his homework. I opened his bedroom door and could not believe what I had saw. There was Aftab casually smoking a cigarette, whilst sitting on his bed with his legs crossed doing his homework. I stormed in and shouted at him, telling him to throw the cigarette away, so he quickly tossed it out of the attic window.

Aftab heartily apologised. He told me he felt stressed and seemed unable to cope. He then made me promise not to tell Dad or Mum. I promised, as long as he didn't smoke again. I lectured Aftab and made him see sense on how dangerous smoking is to his health.

From downstairs, I could hear Mum shouting my name very loudly. She told me to quickly come downstairs as there were a couple of policemen waiting to see me in the shop. My heart sank, thinking the worst. I ran downstairs and there were two policemen with an elderly lady I knew by the name of Cookoo. The lady could not speak English and when she wanted eggs she would make a round shape with her hand and say 'cookoo', hence from that day we called her cookoo.

Cookoo had a habit of twitching her nose. She looked similar to that of a rabbit.

One of the policemen politely said, "This lady tried to run out of the Echo supermarket on Stanley Road. She was ranting and raving as she led us to your shop."

I asked Cookoo what had happened and in sign language she said she was shopping and all of a sudden, a black man grabbed her handbag and ran out of the shop. She anxiously tried to run after him, crying and shouting 'faloos, faloos'. (Faloos meaning money.) She said, with tears rolling down her face, "I tried to tell the policeman that a thief had stolen my handbag and I ran after him shouting, 'faloos faloos' but no one helped in assisting me."

I said to the awaiting policemen, "She is a respectable lady. I have known her for over a year – she is not a thief."

The policemen thanked me for helping them understand what had happened and I pointed to where she lived. I thought it was a boring day. It was an intense and depressive day – I thought that was enough excitement for me today!

May 24th 1972

Mr Reed died

One of my dearest and most loyal customer was a man called Mr Reed. He was very tall, stout and a very friendly jolly Scotsman. He worked at The Royal Bakery in Levenshulme.

Every day without fail when Mr Reed had finished from work he would come into my shop at approximately six o'clock in the evening. Mr Reed would greet me with a jolly laugh then say, "Hello, Malika, how are you today?"

I would say back, "Very well, thank you, Mr Reed."

The first item Mr Reed would ask for was his large tin of Scotch broth soup, then he would ask for his usual packet of cigarettes which was ten Park Drive, plus a large bottle of Lemonade, with one tin of Mixy kitty food. The cat food was for a stray cat known as Jimmy. He fed Jimmy in the garden as his landlord would not allow animals in the flats.

Mr Reed would always ask how all my family were. As usual, my reply would be, "All the family are fine thanks, Mr Reed."

Mr Reed would bring me some small jam and cream cupcakes with cherries on the top in a little white box. He had a very kind nature and I thanked him for his generosity.

After buying his goods Mr Reed would say,

"Goodbye, Malika, see you tomorrow." Then he would give me a little wave and go on his way.

I had become concerned because Mr Reed had failed to come into the shop for over a week. My heart felt low as I thought he may be buying his shopping elsewhere.

A couple of weeks had passed and in walked two tall broad policemen, to buy some canned drinks. (In my experience, when policeman see young pretty girls they like to chat them up and ask them out!)

The younger policeman told me that they had been called out to the large house across the road, where an elderly gentleman had been found deceased. He had been dead for over two weeks.

I told them I had not seen my regular customer Mr Reed for about two weeks and that he lived across the road in that same old house. The policeman looked at me and sadly said, "Sorry love, but it was a Mr Reed who we found deceased. He had collapsed on the floor and was not found until weeks later. His electric heater was still on and it was already very hot weather. The poor man's skin had melted into the floorboards."

I felt upset, as he was one of most polite, and most gentle, caring elderly person I had ever met. God rest his soul, he will be sadly missed.

May 30th 1972

My heart fluttered

Well, luck was on my side, as I had a habit of peeping through the shop window. It was to my good fortune that I saw a young handsome man moving into our neighbourhood. He was the only customer who had ever made my heart flutter. I could see he was tall, handsome and muscular. This man had quickly popped into the shop – he spoke softly and he had blue dreamy eyes. When he looked at me it was as if he was slowly undressing me. My knees would turn to jelly but I had to somehow get these sinful thoughts out of my head. This intelligent, hunky man was dressed immaculately – white shirt, grey suit, black tie, black expensive looking shoes, Rolex watch. He was holding an expensive leather briefcase. I felt like melting into his arms (my imagination had got the better of me). All in all, he was gorgeous!

In a well-spoken manner he said, "Hello, my name is Simon, I've just moved across the road. I've got a job nearby. I am an accountant and it's nice to know that there is a shop close to home that closes late."

I told Simon my name and I welcomed him into the area. Simon bought a small brown bread, a bottle of skimmed milk and some strawberry jam and cheese slices, he paid me the money for the goods and winked at me as he said, "Bye, see you tomorrow." Luckily Dad was not around when Simon came into the shop!

Evening came and I just couldn't wait to see Simon again (think I spoke too soon). Sure enough, Simon came into the shop accompanied by his wife and two young children. Simon proudly introduced me to his Spanish wife Tanya, who was slim, beautiful and elegant, and his lovely children James and Mary (my heart sank). I welcomed the family into our neighbourhood!

I had thought I had met the man of my dreams, but I could not have been more wrong. It was better to have found out now, than much later on.

My imagination had worked overtime, now I came back to reality. Still I will go on to wait for the man of my dreams. That's if he will ever come into Dads Prison Shop.

June 1st 1972

The dog man

Mr Green is an elderly somewhat disabled customer, who walked with a long metal pole which he used as a walking stick (which, in fact, was a long thin metal gas pipe).

I would assume he is in his late seventies. Upon his nose he wore rather large, round thick black glasses. He is tall and slim, has a thin white moustache, and always looked pale and unclean, bless him. He always wore a grey long coat which had a few buttons missing and a cream cowboy hat.

Everybody liked Mr Green because he would look after stray dogs that had been made homeless or had been thrown out by their owners.

Mr Green has a heart of gold and a gentle sympathetic loving nature, as well as being a gentleman. His only downfall is (dare I say it) he really smelt badly of urine.

Looking out of my large overloaded shop window, I could vaguely see Mr. Green coming towards our shop. Well! Here comes Mr Green with his two large brown dogs and his little white mongrel dog. Everyone knew when Mr Green had left the shop because of the bad stench he would leave behind him. Whenever Mr Green came into the shop I would always have a can of the strongest air freshener, just waiting to use when he left the shop. He seemed to leave a bad fishy smell behind him.

Mr Green would always ask me if there was any food which was out of date, or bread I did not want because he could mix the bread into the dog food to make the food go further.

I searched the shop high and low to find anything just to rush him out of the shop, before any other customer came in and became sick from the bad pong coming from Mr Green.

Even Dad knew when Mr Green was in the shop, because of his famous odour, of course! Dad would get breathless, whilst saying in the Punjabi language, "Ikaal baar, badboo bahut hai," meaning for me to hurry up and get him out of the shop before he knocked us out with his smell. Well, that's my dad for you. Sometimes I think Mr Green must understand what Dad says to me because he goes out of the shop with his head down. Poor man, but God bless him for the work he does tirelessly looking after stray dogs.

June 11th 1972

Dad and the old gas van

Our gas van

My old blue rusty Cortina car had outlived its use, in other words it was getting ready for the scrap heap. Dad had promised to buy me a new car and I was still waiting. A few weeks had passed and still there was no mention of a new car. We urgently needed a car to fetch stock for the shop. Dad had been getting lifts to the cash and carry from his very religious cousin Rashid and when he was busy working we did not bother him. Meanwhile, we used to take our large, old corroded pram to the nearest cash and carry to get a little emergency stock. How embarrassing and degrading, ugh.

One warm Saturday afternoon at about two o'clock.

Dad popped his head around the shop door and proudly said, "Look, Malika, I have bought you a fantastic van." I gleamed with excitement and pride but that was until I looked outside, as there in front of my eyes was a blue and white van. It was a retired old gas van. Oh, such humiliation. How could Dad seriously buy me this old dead banger of a gas van? I looked at my dad in utter shame and disgust.

My dad gleamed as he said, "I tell you what! I got the best bargain at that second-hand car auction around the corner. I paid forty-five pounds for that lovely van."

With tears rolling down my face I moaned at Dad, "No way am I going to drive that rubbish old gas van. I would rather die." But with Dad being such a strong dominant man, he made me drive that horrendous ancient gas van!

Dad sat next to me in the passenger seat and told me to drive. I could feel tears slowly and painfully falling down my face. I felt hurt, humiliated and betrayed at driving this evil horror of a van, but I had no choice. Dad's order was his command. I hated my dad for making me drive this old gas van.

The following day, Dad excitedly said, "Don't worry about some of the stains on the van. I have bought three large pots of black gloss paint and two large cheap hand brushes. The van will look fantastic hand painted in black. Your father will make you proud, my lovely daughter." What could I say or do? As I truly could not believe what I had heard. My dad was actually going to paint the van black with a large paint brush, my God, what next!

Dad kept his promise. He quickly painted the gas van black, whilst the drips of lumpy paint were trying desperately to dry up. Once the van was dry, I had no choice but to drive it Anything for a bit of peace. I will be glad when I am out of here and married!

June 21st 1972

Prisoner for ten minutes

Dad was visiting his brother Khan, who lives in Stockport. Mum had gone to see her old friend Sakina. I was once again left all alone in the shop. Dad phoned to say he would be back at the shop for about five o'clock that evening. He told me not to worry.

At about three o'clock Aftab phoned, and said "I am not feeling too well, can you pick me up?"

I irritably said, "I am alone in the shop, so catch the bus."

Aftab panicked. He sorrowfully said that he had lost his small brown wallet and had looked everywhere for it. He cried, "Please, Malika, pick me up. I've got stomach-ache and have been feeling sick and dizzy."

Well, I had no choice I had to lock the shop door. I got my car keys and closed down the shutters. I knew I would be back within fifteen to twenty minutes.

I had just arrived at Aftab's high school. Aftab was waiting patiently outside, with his school bag in his right hand. He looked very pale. I told him to get into the car and then we would go to the doctors in the evening.

Upon arriving at the shop, I pressed the remote control for the shutters to rise. What happened next was alarming as well as shocking. Behind the shop door stood a frail, pale, traumatised elderly lady dressed in white. (At first, I thought it was a ghost.) The lady was in shock, and said, "I was locked in the shop and I am a diabetic. I thought you must have gone home and locked the shop for the day." I heartily apologised and told her when I had left the shop I had not seen anyone come into the shop.

The lady was polite, as well as humorous, and she said, "If I would have to stay here overnight, at least there is food and drink here." At least she saw the funny side of what had happened to her. To this lady it must have felt like hours (but it was only about fifteen minutes). I asked the lady her name. She politely said, "My name is Anna." She also said, "I have not taken anything, you can look in my bag."

I said, "No, dear, I trust you."

She said, "You can look on your security cameras."

I said, "It's alright," and that I was sorry about locking her accidentally in the shop.

Anna said, "I was banging on the shutters but nobody could hear me. I wanted to phone my son but thought, how could he possibly get me out from behind the shutters?"

Anna laughed so much and I laughed with her. I gave Anna some groceries as a goodwill gesture for the trauma she had been through, she smiled and then went on her way. I thought never again, if I had to ever leave the shop in a hurry I would look all around the shop, even behind and under the counter. That poor lady, what must she have felt being locked up like a prisoner. Phew! What an embarrassing and unusual day.

June 25th 1972

Dad and the stolen chocolates

Dad had bought some chocolate boxes from a man by the name of Charlie. The chocolates were selling cheap (in other words, stolen chocolates). There were about twenty boxes, each box contained ten bars of chocolates. I asked Dad why he had bought all those chocolates. I told him that only one store sold the chocolates, Hollander, but would dad listen? No, he would not.

A few weeks had passed, and then one Thursday evening two tall broad frightening men came into the shop and spoke to Dad. They were detectives enquiring about the chocolate bars in the shop.

One of the men said firmly, "There has been a report that there are stolen chocolates being sold on these premises, a certain brand of chocolates that Hollander in the town centre only sells." Dad invited the detectives into the living room. They asked Dad who he had bought the chocolates from? Dad innocently pointed towards me, whilst I thought oh my God, what should I do or say! The detectives then started to question me.

I was lucky I had an innocent baby-looking face. I was asked from where and from whom I had purchased these chocolates. I imagined a drama unfold within my head. I naively said, "I was busy cleaning the shelves in the shop and a salesman came into the shop. He showed me some samples of a brand-new chocolate bar in different flavours, which were selling wildly in the other shops. He also gave me a sample to try. I thought the chocolates were very tasty and I ordered twenty boxes. The salesman told me he would be back in a few seconds as his car was parked on the main road, due to the road works outside my shop. I said 'Fair enough'. Soon he was back with the boxes of chocolates. I then asked him how much? The salesman politely said, 'Forty pounds, please'. I gave him the cash and asked him for the receipt. He said that his receipt book is in the car and that he would bring the receipt straight back. But the salesman never came back."

The detectives told me that they would come back the following day and would bring some photographs for me to see if I could recognise anyone from the photos. The next day in the evening, sure enough, the detectives came again. They had with them lots of photographs, most of the people I recognised because they lived a few streets away and were my regular customers. (I was shocked to see they had been in some sort of trouble with the law.) I told the detectives I did not recognise anyone on the photographs.

Before leaving the detectives said, "If you can remember anything else, could you phone on us on this number."

I said, "Of course, I am a law-abiding citizen." The detectives then went on their way.

I took one look at my dad and said, "You have done it again, now you're getting me into trouble!

What type of dad are you?"

Dad looked at me and apologised. He knew that I could get myself out of complicated situations! But this situation was even more dangerous than I anticipated, as I could have been locked up in prison for buying stolen chocolates. I was thinking in my heart, please Dad, change for the better, if that was at all possible!

June 30th 1972

Ferzana met Nathan

Ferzana had started a part-time job as a receptionist at the local chemist around the corner. In the late afternoon, she would help us in the shop.

Ferzana was helping me clean the shelves in the shop, whilst moaning loudly, as usual, then in walks this tall, dark handsome man by the name of Nathan. He had moved to England from Jamaica ten years previously; he said he worked at a computer firm repairing computers.

Within ten minutes he had told us his life story (how boring). He was neatly dressed as well as being a very smooth talker. I felt he had won the hearts of many women.

I told Ferzana I had to urgently go to the cash and carry, because the cheese block had finished. I took Mariam along with me, as she liked to swoon over the delicious sweets in the cash and carry. Ferzana stayed to look after the shop. Nathan stayed behind to talk to Ferzana...

Two hours had quickly passed and as I entered the shop what did I see? Nathan still chatting happily to my sister (I think it was time for him to go home!).

Four months passed by peacefully, yet I had noticed that Ferzana was always going out and coming back late. She was making excuses that she was given overtime at work. I remember this occasion very well. Ferzana was crying and I asked her what was wrong. (My God was I in for a shock.) Ferzana anxiously said, "I can't tell you. I feel so ashamed." I told her that we were sisters and that she could discuss anything and everything with me. Ferzana put her face in her hands and cried once again whilst she pitifully said, "I am pregnant, and I don't know what to do."

I angrily said, "The first thing that is going to happen is the family will disown you. The next, Dad will secretly kill you." I had to think quickly. I asked her whose baby she was carrying.

She said, "Nathan's."

I was utterly shocked and shouted, "You what! Ferzana, how much more shame can you bring upon us all?" I advised her to go to her doctor, as everything told to her was in complete privacy and confidential. The doctor could not tell Dad about her being pregnant. She would have to tell the doctor she wanted an abortion, just tell the doctor everything that has happened to her, as the doctor knew what Dad was like. She knew he would probably murder her.

The doctor made an urgent appointment for Ferzana to have an abortion, but we had to be careful that Dad did not find out.

The date had now arrived for Ferzana's abortion, but what excuse could we make to Dad? I told Dad that we were going to a friend's party as she was about to get married very soon, and that we would be back a little late. Dad said, "Out of all my children you are the one whom I trust the most, but try to be back soon, your mum will worry till you get back." I felt awful lying to Dad, but my sister Ferzana meant a lot to me and I did not want Dad to hurt her.

The day had come, off we went to the hospital as I silently consoled and comforted Ferzana. I kept reassuring her that I would always be there for her. Sometimes I wondered why it was always Fersana who got herself into troublesome situations.

I sat uncomfortably in the waiting room and prayed Ferzana would be fine. After an agonising wait Ferzana came out of the doctor's room looking weak and pale. I guaranteed her that everything would go smoothly at home, just to go upstairs to her bedroom and act as though nothing had happened and get plenty of rest.

As for myself, I felt more exhausted than Ferzana, but at least Ferzana never got into that kind of trouble again. As for that coward Nathan, he had left our area. I hope I never set eyes on that sex beast again, he was more mouse than a man. I don't know how many more women he had made pregnant, loving them and leaving them. I hope Nathan never finds peace on this earth. He will meet a woman who will do the dirty on him and he will suffer. As for Ferzana, she has slowly changed her wild ways, thank God!

July 2nd 1972

My mother's adopted son

A young slim, good looking Asian man casually come into the shop, but for some reason he was behaving a bit oddly. He asked nervously, "Can I err I mean if you don't mind can I have a can of lemonade and a Bounty chocolate bar or I may change it to a Mars bar?" His hands shook as he paid me the money and then he said tearfully, "My name is Aslam. I live around the corner with my mother, but she died a month ago. I miss her so much." His tears were flowing like a river from his heartbroken eyes.

I called out to my mother, "Mum, can you come into the shop, please?"

Mum came running into the shop. "What's happened? Is everything alright, Malika?" said my distraught mother, looking at the young man crying.

The young man looked at my mother and weepily said, "Sorry, Auntie, I miss my mother so much. I have no other relatives and my social worker said I suffer from slight autism." His hands shook and what happened next shocked me.

My mother grabbed the young man's hand with love and care in her eyes and said, "I am here for you, son. Don't worry, you are welcome here anytime." Then she put her hand on his head and patted his head slowly.

The young man tearfully said to Mum, "My name is Aslam, I have no one here." He wiped away his tears from his large pining eyes saying, "Thank you, Auntie and God bless you. My mother died of a heart attack in hospital and I stayed indoors crying and depressed. I didn't feel like going out as people would point and laugh at me. I am a human being and have feelings." Then suddenly, without warning, Aslam fell upon my mother's feet and kissed them. My mother picked him up, grabbed his hand and took him indoors to meet Dad.

Dad was sleeping on the sofa and snoring loudly. Mum woke him up and told him about Aslam. Dad's heart melted as he spoke to Aslam, he felt so sorry for him (yes, dad has a heart ha ha). Smiling, Dad said, "We are your family. You are welcome here anytime." Aslam started to shake nervously and cried on Dad's shoulder.

Well, here comes our adopted brother! And Mum's adopted son, Aslam.

July 3rd 1972

The cute little dog called Mikey

James is a nice short middle-aged gentleman, he has two front teeth missing which was very noticeable. He would always talk about the time he lived in America, working as an engineer. He would tell me he was a black belt in karate and that he could handle himself in many situations he would go on and on. (I am sure he kept repeating himself, or worst still, he may have had dementia?)

James would always carry Mikey into the shop (mainly for hygiene reasons) Mikey was my favourite little customer, he is a small, brown well-groomed terrier dog. He was so cute, especially when he growls, grrrrr.

I loved teasing Mikey. I would slowly walk up towards James, whilst Mikey would have his beady doggy eyes looking strictly at me, it was as though he was warning me to keep away or face his doggy biting wrath? I even tried to bribe Mikey with some chocolate buttons but Mikey was not having it. Mikey was adamant no one went near his owner, sometimes I wondered who owned who?

A week later James came into the shop. As usual he was carrying Mikey. He told me Mikey had a bit of an operation on his right eye. As I went to look at his eye, Mikey growled loudly then slowly leading to a howl, then another bad-tempered growl. I would giggle hysterically, he was such an adorable small dog with an amusing loud snarl. Where did that dog get its energy from?

James told me that Mikey had become a dad to a litter of four puppies, let's hope that doggy fatherhood had calmed small Mikey down.

July 6th 1972

The health inspector came today

Ferzana and Aftab were reluctantly helping me to clean the shop freezer and the large cooler. Ferzana was shaking with fright in case she broke one of her well-manicured long nails! (Typical, her beauty had to come first.)

A few hours later, a stricken faced middle-aged gentleman had come into the shop. He wore a black pinstriped suit, white shirt and a black silk tie. He had large wide protruding eyes and was carrying an old brown leather briefcase. The man asked whether he could speak to the occupier or the manager of the premises, he said he was the health inspector. (Oh, Dad, I hope for your sake everything is clean.) Health inspectors have to visit all shops to make sure the shops are safe and hygienically clean.

Dad had just woken up and he came wearily into the shop. The health inspector said, "Mr. Ali, can I have a look around your shop to make sure everything is clean and that there are no health hazards?"

Sure enough, the health inspector looked in the kitchen to see if it was clean. He looked to see if there was soap to wash one's hands with, he looked to see if there was a nail brush near the sink, he looked in the shop to see if everything was clean, and that there were no signs of mice or mice droppings. Believe it or not, the health inspector was happy with the hygiene of the shop and passed us for cleanliness.

I could not help noticing that the health inspector had his beady eyes on my sister Ferzana, whilst Ferzana kept looking at him (the bitch). Ferzana wore a pink low top blouse, dark blue tight-fitting jeans, and black cowboy boots. She looked beautiful, just stunning. That was probably the reason the health inspector hadn't noticed much of the mess and dirt behind the counter! He had his roving eyes on Ferzana.

At least Ferzana in her own way had saved the day, or Dad would have got fined for the shop not being very clean. The health inspector wrote something in his report book. He then gave a slip of paper to Ferzana with his home telephone number, and said "if there are any problems contact me on my personal number"

Before leaving happily out of the shop, the health inspector looked at Ferzana, shook her hand, gave her a cheeky wink and a nod and said bye, but Aftab was not amused at the inspector fancying his elder sister. Well, who cares as Ferzana had honestly saved the day.

July 11th 1972

What's in the envelope?

Ten o'clock at night and all our family were watching the news on the television. People were being told to be aware of strange parcels coming through the post because there had been lots of bomb scares, as tiny bombs were put in parcels through letter boxes and sent to people's houses to harm them.

One week later, a small strange-looking parcel had come through the post. The parcel was wrapped in white flower packaging. Aftab slowly shook the parcel – it sounded like there was a small object inside. Aftab nervously called to Mum, whilst in a state of panic. he said, "Mum, be careful, don't open the parcel. It might have a small letter bomb inside!"

Aftab was acting strangely, he tried to push the dangerous parcel into our next-door neighbour's letter box. I quickly snatched the parcel off Aftab, I then tried to investigate as to what may be inside the parcel. I decided not take any chances and phoned the police.

Sure enough the police came quickly, also most of my nosy neighbours came out to look at what was going on. One short policeman held a small metal detector, whilst the other policeman slowly and very carefully started to unpack the suspicious parcel. The parcel was carefully opened, and surprisingly, one of the policemen started to laugh. Inside the parcel was a bottle of tooth whitener that Aftab had ordered from a magazine. I could have killed Aftab for causing us all so much confusion and embarrassment. The policeman patiently said, "Better to be safe than sorry."

The nosy neighbours standing outside started laughing when they saw what had come out of the parcel, and to think Aftab was putting the parcel into next door 's letter box! I told Aftab off and strictly told him, "Don't order anything from magazines or catalogues. You must let me know first."

What a hectic day, if it's not one member of the family causing commotions it's another.

Roll on tomorrow, don 't know what tomorrow will bring, God help us.

July 12th

My friend Ruby

Such a cool calm day, feeling a bit bored, just eating chocolates again. Oh, yes, I seem to be putting the weight upon my thighs. I thought I would just go for a brisk walk at the local park.

Ready steady go, this is as brisk as I can walk, just puffing and panting been around once. I thought I would go around again, when suddenly from behind I heard a soft voice call out,
     "Hello, Malika." I quickly turned around and there in front of me was my old school friend Ruby. We just hugged each other tightly (we were best of friends in junior school) but we had lost contact with each other, because we went to different high schools.

We both sat on the brown park bench. I looked at Ruby – I could see hurt and pain in her eyes. I gently asked her if everything was alright. Ruby's tears flowed down like a waterfall. Ruby sadly put her head down and said, "Malika, I have been married nearly three years now. I have a beautiful daughter called Shamma, she is two years old. I left home and got married to Jamal Khan. I thought he was the perfect man and loved me so much, but everything seems to have changed as time passed by. After a couple of months of marriage, a letter arrived for Jamal. I opened the letter and enclosed was a photo of a pretty young woman with her arm around Jamal, whilst she was also holding her young child in the other arm. There was also a letter written in Urdu. I could not read Urdu, so I took it to my cousin Salmah, she is married with two children.

"Salmah was cooking a lovely meat curry, you could smell the aroma outside her house, but she kindly stopped cooking and read Jamal's letter for me, whilst later translating all to me. Believe me, the words that came out of her mouth utterly shocked me. I just wanted to hide my head under a stone and not come out. Salmah's tears flowed as she shouted, 'Ruby, what have you done? You have married a married man who has one child. This is Jamal's wife writing this letter to him. She wrote how much she loves him and cannot wait to see him when he comes back over to Pakistan. Oh my God, he's a bloody BIGAMIST! He married you to get his indefinite stay in this country, get rid of him, or report him to the police or immigration," Ruby cried out loudly.

Ruby cried as she said, "Malika, my mind was in a daze. I could not go back to my parents home, I did not want shame to come upon my family. Also, I did not want anyone laughing at me. Now I have a daughter, I have to think about her. She loves her father so much. Jamal is a bully, when someone has upset him, he used to shout and beat me black and blue, but I still stayed with him, thinking one day he would change. What else can I do? Sorry, Malika, for giving you all this tension. I just don't know what else to do."

I told Ruby anytime she needed help she knew where I lived, and that my father owned a shop called Ali's Shop and she was welcome anytime. Ruby hugged me again and went on her way.

Two weeks had passed, and into our shop walked Ruby, holding her two-year-old child in her arms. She had bruises upon her face and arms, and said, "Malika, Jamal beat me up again, just don't know what to do? I stay mostly for my child's sake, if it was not for my child I would have committed suicide."

I called my dad into the shop and told him about Ruby's husband, Dad asked me where her husband worked and Ruby told Dad that Jamal worked at a restaurant called Aziz take-away on Wilmslow Road.

Dad stormed off in a temper to Jamal's place of work. He waited half an hour for Jamal to finish work and followed him to his house. Jamal was about to enter his house when Dad shouted loudly, "Hey, Jamal, come here, I want a word with you. I hear you beat your wife up. You don't know who the fuck I am. I will finish you if you ever lay another hand on Ruby ever again, or I will call the immigration people and get you deported. I am warning you, everyone knows me in Manchester; they also know my brothers who are all gangsters. I am watching you, so be careful. I don't ever want to find out you have beaten your wife up again or you will be a dead man." Then Dad went angrily on his way home.

Dad had calmed down as he entered the shop and told us what had happened. He looked at Ruby sympathetically he said, "Ruby, you are like my daughter, if Jamal bullies you again, you come here and then he will feel my famous danda on his head."

Ruby hugged Dad and wholeheartedly thanked him. With tears of joy, Ruby went home. After half an hour, she phoned me and said, "Jamal has changed, he even made a cup of tea for me. Now he speaks kindly to me as well. Please thank Uncle for his help, you are all so caring towards me I love you all."

From that day Jamal had changed. (Jamal had found out from his place of work, that Dad was part of a family of gangsters. His workmates told Jamal to be careful and watch his back-ha ha!)

Once again, Dad's danda saved the day. Love you, Dad.

July 15th 1972

My hair was getting thinner

Over the next few months, due to severe stress, I noticed my hair seemed to be getting thinner. I phoned my hairdresser for an appointment for a tight hair perm, hoping that the perm would make my hair look thicker. I was told to come on Thursday at two o'clock in the afternoon.

Thursday soon arrived. I felt so excited, Mum had given me ten pounds to pay for my hair to be permed. I had asked Ferzana and Mum to look after the shop whilst I popped down to the hairdressers. I didn't need the car, as the hairdresser was only around the corner.

Upon reaching the hair salon I was sat in that damn hairdresser's chair for ages – it felt like hours had gone past. Then hey presto! My permed hair was absolutely fantastic, my tight perm made my hair look and feel thicker. I couldn't wait to rush back to the shop to show my family. (I even gave the hairdresser a one pound tip, because I was so happy with my beautiful perm.)

Upon entering the shop Ferzana and Mum took one look at me and started to laugh hysterically. Ferzana told me that I looked like one of the famous old Marx brothers, the one with the curly white bushy hair who could not talk!

Miriam came home from school, she was shocked

when she saw my hair. She could not stop giggling. I was so upset that I yelled at my rude sisters and walked tearfully into the back room.

A few days had passed and I was getting used to my new permed hair. I actually bought myself an afro comb, it was hard controlling my hair but I got used to it. Four of my regular, teenage school children had come into the shop for chocolates; they looked at my hair and started giggling and pointing at me. One of them said, "You look like that cartoon character on the jam jar, ha ha."

I eventually let my hair perm grow out (many people thought that I was of mixed race) instead of Asian. Thin hair or not, that was the first and last time I would ever have my hair permed.

July 19th 1972

Uncle Karim and Auntie Betty are visiting again

Dad's younger brother and wife are coming to visit us today, but Dad, for some unknown reason, dislikes his younger brother Karim and his English sister-in-law Betty. Uncle Karim is stocky and heavily built, he also has lizard green eyes and wears large brown spectacles. Auntie Betty is really pretty. She has a bit of temper so Dad better be careful. She is tall, has blonde short curly hair, she is very dominant and bossy. (In their relationship, you know who wears the trousers.)

Uncle Karim has a very bad habit of taking home most of our stock from the shop without paying! Uncle Karim and Auntie Betty are very careful on how and where they spend their money. They never bought Mum anything as a kind gesture for preparing a lovely meal for them (not even a cheap box of chocolates). Auntie Betty, whenever she goes home, is always given twenty pounds from my mother to spend on herself. Now here they come one by one, the unwelcome relatives have arrived. Dad invites Auntie and Uncle into the warm unwelcoming lounge. Mum has prepared a delicious dinner. She cooked kebabs, chicken plough, meat curry, and for dessert, apple pie and custard.

Uncle Karim and Auntie Betty stayed over for four hours, and then they were ready to go home. I always gave Dad two pounds (from the till, of course) for giving Uncle and Auntie a lift home. I had to tell Dad a lie that Auntie Betty had given me two pounds to get a lift home in our four-seater van.

On this occasion Dad had caught me taking out two pounds from the till, and curiously asked me what I was going to buy. Or was I giving him the money towards the lift for Uncle and Auntie? (Dad then somehow knew Auntie Betty had never ever given me money for the lifts.) Dad crossly told Uncle and Auntie to catch the bus as petrol was too expensive.

What could I say, Dad was annoyed with me having to lie to him, but he forgave me.

Sure enough, the same way Uncle and Auntie had come to visit us the same way they had to go, only this time empty-handed with no free stock from our shop. Ha ha

July 24th 1972

Miriam was bullied at school

Miriam had been behaving very strangely; she either had stomach-ache or toothache. Then the next day she was having headaches and so on. Any excuse for her not to attend school.

Miriam had already missed one week of school, even though she looked well, but by the end of each evening she would be happily playing on her game board. She was laughing, giggling and skipping. Dad and Mum were by now thinking something was very wrong. Dad asked me to have a word with Miriam and find out what was upsetting her.

Monday morning arrived. I looked at Miriam and asked her why she was lying about being ill once again and that she must tell me the truth. Miriam wiped away her tears as she sadly explained to me that she was getting bullied by a certain girl at school; this girl was one year older and for no reason at all she had targeted Miriam to bully.

I asked Miriam for the bully's name and she said, "Her name is Sally. It is that girl who comes in for cheese and crackers, the one with a pink and silver hair band. She also wears silver laced up heeled boots."

Firmly I said to Miriam, "I will not go into your school and report Sally, but I will have to have a word with her when she comes into our shop."

Sure enough, the next day this bully had come into our shop. She came mostly at the same time every day. When she came into the shop, I locked the shop door and told her off. I warned her that if she ever bullied Miriam again, I would bully her so very badly and that she would remember my bullying all her life. The girl was frightened and promised not to bully Miriam again, but when Sally arrived at her home she told her Mum and Dad what had happened in the shop.

Ten minutes later Sally's dad came fuming and swearing at me inside the shop. He rudely told me off.

My dad was standing near the shop freezer, upon hearing this man shouting at me, he picked up his danda and said angrily to the man, "Have you come for trouble? I am waiting for your move."

The man was shaking as he apologised and said, "It must have been a misunderstanding, my daughter will never bully Miriam again."

Well! From that day Miriam was never bullied again.

Dad's thick long danda stick had come in handy to me. Thank God that man apologised to me or Dad would have had another grievous bodily harm case against him and would have been locked up for hitting that man.

At least Miriam is much happier going to school after all that tremendous hassle we all had to go through. Phew!

July 30th 1972

I found out I had a stepbrother

Dad is my number one hero. He had never lied to any of his children or kept secrets from us all. (Now I know better, how wrong could I have been?)

One warm peaceful evening, a young, handsome, light-skinned Asian man came into the shop. He politely asked for dad. I asked him his name and he said, "My name is Tariq Ali." I told him that Dad had gone out, and he would be coming back in a few hours and if he could call back later.

Dad came back two hours later. He was absolutely exhausted. I said, "Dad, a young man named Tariq Ali had been asking about you," but for some odd reason Dad did not look too surprised. Dad had a sinister and happy smile upon his face (I thought, *hold on a minute, is he trying to arrange a marriage for one of his daughters?*) Dad spoke to me in confidence and said, "Tariq is my son from a previous relationship." I was in shock as well as excited, having found out that I had another brother, but then I wondered what would Mum say about Dad betraying her in the past?

I told Mum about Tariq. I had no idea Mum already knew about Tariq. Everything had been hidden and this was a family secret that the brothers and sisters had never known about!

Well! Sure enough, after two hours in walks my stepbrother. I loudly and impatiently called out to Dad to come into the shop.

My dad's eyes lit up as he hugged this young man. Dad introduced me to Tariq and I was so overwhelmed. We started talking and found out that we had so much in common (especially my dad). The rest of the family accepted Tariq, but Mum still tried to stay out of the way when Tariq came to visit us. As for Dad, nothing would surprise me. Next, I may have another sister or brother waiting to be introduced to us. Well, only time can tell.

August 1ˢᵗ 1972

Aftab and his friend

Aftab had rushed from school. He was breathless and looked very worried. I asked him what the matter was and he gloomily said, "Shahid, my best friend, lost his father over five years ago, and his uncle shouts and bullies him. I want to help him but I don't know what to do?"

Shahid is short in height and very thin, he is a very polite lad, but he seemed very weary and tense of people and his surroundings.

I told Aftab if he got involved in Shahid's problems, he would get blamed in the end by his family, but Aftab said, "Please, Malika, we have to help him somehow!"

I told Aftab to tell Shahid's teacher, Mrs Norton, what was going on in his household. He had to tell her about all the bullying which was affecting Shahid mentally and physically.

Shahid must protect himself as he already was abused and harassed.

The next day after school, Aftab came home with Shahid who looked very upset and distressed. Shahid did not want to go home. I said, "Don't worry, we will try and sort all this mess out. First of all, what is the name and phone number of your doctor?" Shahid gave me all the information and details that I had needed.

An appointment had been made for Shahid the following day at five thirty in the afternoon. Shahid was accompanied by myself and Aftab. The doctor had known about the severe health problems that Shahid had been suffering. He is a disabled child and stuttered, and he also suffered from panic attacks. It was now Shahid's turn to go in to see the doctor. I told the doctor what had been going on in his home and the doctor was very concerned about Shahid's health. The doctor thanked me for letting this problem come to his attention and that he would contact social services and let them know what had been happening in the case of Shahid Akhtar.

Well, I said to Aftab and Shahid, let's see what happens now? The ball was rolling.

If nothing got done Dad would have to go around and sort his uncle out. Dad was already known around our area as a tough rough man that nobody would ever try to mess about with. People were afraid of Dad. But let's hope it does not come to that or come to my dad's special danda.

One week later Aftab and Shahid came happily home from school. Shahid told me that a lady from social services had come to his house, there was a meeting and his uncle had been sorted out. His social worker, Anne, told his uncle if there were any more mental or physical abuse upon Shahid, the police would be getting involved. From that day onwards his uncle had been kind and considerate to him (thank God). One problem solved.

Please, Aftab, no more problems. We have enough of our own.

August 6th 1972

The neighbours from hell

Dad was in such a good mood, he was even singing (but I think I spoke too soon). Some new neighbours had moved into our area – a Romanian family, husband and wife and their four naughty, mischievous children aged between four and twelve.

Well! Believe me, my dad's life was made hell since they had moved into our area. The children looked so sweet, little had Dad known that the four of them were stealing sweets and food every day from our shop. I had noticed Dad seemed to be smoking more and moaning more. His personality had completely changed since those neighbours from hell had moved into our area

One day Dad saw the twelve-year-old girl, who had untidy hair, put a can of orange soda inside her trousers. The youngest girl with the dirty nose put a large bar of Whole Nut chocolate and small bars of chocolates up her sleeve.

Dad was simply furious, he told the girls to get the sweets and drink out of where they had put them or he would phone the police. The children were so embarrassed that they handed back the goods they had stolen. Dad banned the children from our shop

A few days later the parents of the naughty children came into the shop, pushing a small dirty blue pram with a youngster sleeping comfortably inside. We have a medium-sized glass cabinet, and on the top shelf were displayed watches and jewellery. When the children's parents left the shop, I quickly noticed three diamante watches were missing, as well as most of the rings, earrings and necklaces. The parents were professional thieves as they had stolen most of the jewellery at the blink of an eye.

It was a bit too late to accuse the Romanian people of stealing. When my dad saw the Romanian family passing our shop he popped his head outside the shop and shouted out to them, "I do not need your custom and you are not allowed in this shop again. You are nothing but thieves."

It was obvious that the children's parents had told them to steal from our shop. Four weeks later the family from hell had finally moved out of the area. That was when my dad felt so much at peace; nobody had made my dad feel so nervous in his life like that Romanian family from hell.

August 12th 1972

Aftab is out of order

Aftab had been acting very strange lately, he was using every excuse in the book to go out. Recently he had been smelling of strong shaving lotion, ugh. I actually thought he may have a girlfriend. I had also noticed that recently boxes of chocolates were disappearing of the shelves. Well, now I know why.

Aftab had, on a few occasions, been sneaking out at night and coming home late. Dad somehow had found out about Aftab's sneaky ways, so one cold drizzly night Dad decided to follow Aftab to see what he was up to. What Dad saw truly upset and confused him. Aftab was smoking with a few young yobs and a few unruly swearing girls, then Aftab and his friends walked into a pub called Walter's Pub. Dad could hear the owner of the pub ask Aftab and his friends their age. Aftab calmly said, "I am nineteen years old."

Dad heard what Aftab had cheekily said and instantly ran up to Aftab and gave him such a slap on his face whilst shouting, "You bastard, you are humiliating your family. You have become such a rebel. I will give you rebel when you get home."

Aftab pulled and then pushed his hand away from Dad and ran quickly off down the street. Dad tried to chase him but became dizzy and breathless. Dad looked around for Aftab, he then started to panic – *what if someone hurts him, or tries to kidnap him.*

There are a lot of perverts about!

Dad went home alone, upset, with tears rolling down his pathetic face. He woke Mum up and told her what had happened. Mum would not stop crying, thinking the worst that could have happened to her son; whether he had been beaten up by racists and so on. The more she thought the more she cried.

Early the next morning, Mum asked me to help her look for Aftab, so I quickly got the car keys, and drove Mum to look around for him. At first, we tried to guess which friend he might be staying with, then suddenly I told my mum Stuart Shaw who lived in Didsbury. He must have gone there. I told Mum to calm down and I promised her that everything would be alright.

Rain was pouring down on the windscreen as I drove up to Didsbury. The windscreen wipers were not working properly and needed replacing but I just about managed to reach our destination.

I recalled a few months previously picking Aftab up from an address - 23 Rowlands Road, in Didsbury. Slowly but surely, we reached the address and I quickly got out of my car. I was a bit nervous! I prayed Aftab was staying at Stuart's house. I rang the bell, then a tall elderly lady opened the door, and she said, "Oh! have you come for Aftab?"

I calmly said, "Yes, he is my brother. Our mum is in the car, she has been crying and worrying all night for him."

A few seconds later Aftab appeared. He said, "I am not coming home to Dad. He is always moaning and shouting. I can't take it anymore. All I did was hang around with a few friends trying to enjoy myself."

I sternly said to Aftab, "They are not your friends. They smoke and take drugs, plus they are leading you onto the wrong path. You know how much Mum loves you, she nearly had a heart attack last night. Please think of Mum, as you only have the one mother."

Aftab put his head down in shame because he had broken his mother's heart. He rushed to the car, hugged mum and cried on her shoulder, and well, at least he was back in the car. I thanked Stuart's mum from the bottom of my heart, then we headed back to the Prison Shop.

When we eventually reached the shop, Dad was waiting outside with his danda. He did not speak to Aftab. As the saying goes: Silence speaks louder than words.

In the back-room Dad looked angrily at Aftab, then Aftab turned his head away and hugged Mum. Aftab sat with Mum for an hour till Dad had eventually calmed down.

Then Aftab got up and walked over to Dad and apologised for his bad behaviour, and promised that this type of occurrence would never happen again.

Dad kissed Aftab on his right cheek and gave him a tight hug. Dad lovingly said, "Never leave like that again. Anything could have happened to you. As you know, all your family love you so much."

I then saw the softer and sensitive side of my dad, how sweet. My brother was back we were one loving family again.

August 17th 1972

Mum's gossipy cousin Ruxana

Mum is in such a blissful mood, mainly because her favourite cousin Ruxana is coming to visit her today, along with her baby Rahim, who is only five months old. Mum has been busy in the kitchen for hours preparing Ruxana's favourite meal, which consisted of Chicken biryani, meat and potato curry, samosas, potato cutlets and for dessert there is semolina pudding and jelly and cream, yummy.

Auntie Ruxana arrived with her baby Rahim at one o'clock in the afternoon. Auntie Ruxsana is short in height, I would say she was about four foot two inches tall. She is grossly obese and her belly bounces up and down when she laughs. Auntie's downfall is her wild temper – if one laughs at her then they will feel the other side of her fists, but she is lovely in every other way. Auntie came up to me casually at the counter where I stood, she looked up at me as I nervously said, "As Salaam o-alakum, Auntie."

She replied, "Walakum Salaam." Then Auntie said, "Malika, have you found any eligible bachelor you wish to marry? Make sure if you find a good man, that he is kind and rich. It does not matter if he is not handsome!" Auntie winked at me and then followed the delicious aroma that was in the air and walked straight into the kitchen, then she quickly walked into the living room where Mum waited to greet her with open arms.

164

Auntie happily said, "As Salaam o alakum Baji." (Baji meaning older sister.)

Mum hugged her and excitedly said, "Walakum Salaam." Mum took Auntie into the kitchen where the food was displayed and ready to eat. The kitchen table was set so wonderfully, plus there was a large bunch of red roses in a long slim glass vase. Auntie Ruxana gleamed with pleasure whilst looking at all the food that Mum had prepared for her. Mum's food is known to be popular throughout all the relatives for being the tastiest, scrumptious and the most nutritious.

After dinner Mum and Auntie sat in the living room giving each other the latest gossip! Auntie Ruxana impatiently said, "Baji, my brother-in-law Saleem, lives in the flat opposite our flat in Didsbury. He has two children, Shazia is six years old and his son Shezad is four years old. Well, Baji, his wife Sophia goes out to college at nine in the morning till six in the evening leaving her husband Saleem, who by the way is unemployed as he had become redundant, baby-sitting the children. He is their child minder, it's disgusting and do you know, when my husband Tariq goes to work at seven in the morning his brother Saleem knocks on my flat door and asks if he can leave the children with me for a few hours, and now Baji, I am getting so fed up I am considering telling Tariq to look for another flat. It is just ridiculous. Look, I have a five-month-old baby and I also need a rest as I am a diabetic.

"Saleem's wife Sophia is enjoying herself. I am

telling you, Baji, I am convinced that Sophia is having an affair. Sometimes I look from my flat window and I can see a blue car with a man driving near our road, and then he reverses around the corner of our road to let Sophia out. Believe me, Baji I truly believe there is another man on the scene, but I dare not tell Tariq, then he will tell Saleem then I will get into trouble. I tell you, I have never liked Sophia, there is something weird about her. Sorry to stress you but I had to tell someone close to me. I just don't know what to do?

"Also, do you know all she cooks for Saleem is lentil curry, and tin fish pilchards curry and occasionally jelly and custard. The bitch is saving money for her family in Pakistan. I cook nice food for my husband – meat curry, chicken curry veg curry. Sophia cooks the same old cheap food, one curry lasting her three to four days, the lazy woman. I have to give Saleem meat curry and left-over chapattis of Tariq's. What type of wife is she?"

Mum thought for a second and said patiently, "Ruxana, don't get upset. Try to stay calm, leave all up to the Almighty God."

Four hours had passed, Auntie was getting tired and said, "Baji, I will have to depart now, my husband Saleem is coming back home from work soon."

Mum and Auntie Ruxana hugged each other, Mum gave her a kiss on her cheek and Auntie wholeheartedly thanked Mum for everything. Mum held auntie's right hand and put forty pounds in her palm for her to buy her baby a present. Auntie thanked Mum and went on her way.

Well, Auntie what a sob story and you're forty pounds better off, what more could Auntie Ruxana wish for, ha ha.

August 21st 1972

The wife abuser

Our next-door neighbours are really nice (well that's what I thought, I couldn't have been more wrong.) My lovely helpful kind neighbour Christine lived just next door. Christine is short in height, petite and spoke with a soft angelic voice. Her long dark mousy brown hair is always brushed back into a neat long plait. My dear friend Christine was sometimes prone to panic attacks (with hyperactive children like hers, anyone would have a panic attack.)

One cold dark winter's night Christine came sadly into our shop. Upon looking at her face (I could see the hurt and abuse in her eyes, she also had a sore black reddish eye) I asked her what had happened. With her head bowed down she quietly said, "Tommy, my mischievous hyperactive young son, was playing with his cricket ball, he then accidentally threw the ball at my face, which hit my eye."

I had no doubt in my mind that Christine was telling me a lie. Five days later an identical incident happened. Christine had another black eye and a rather large bandage wrapped around her wrist. I sympathetically asked Christine, "What's going on, love?"

Christine tearfully said, "I slipped on a banana skin and accidentally hurt my hand."

I now knew my friend was lying to me; she was

hurting painfully, mentally and physically. What could I say or do? Christine would not wholly confide in me.

Ferzana came home from work, I then gave her all the sad news and told her that I had a suspicion that Christine's husband was mentally and physically abusing her. Ferzana is Christine's best friend. She was surprised that Christine had not confided in her, especially in her time of need.

Ferzana decided to call around at Christine's house whilst Christine's husband Jimmy was out of the house. He had gone to the pub as usual. Ferzana was shocked to see Christine in such excruciating pain. Christine opened her heart and soul out to Ferzana. She told her what Jimmy kept doing to her, and that he was drinking too much alcohol, plus he was dating other women. He was not giving her any money for food or other vital expenses, and she did not know what to do. She also feared for her children's' safety.

Ferzana hugged and tried to console Christine whilst saying, "Don't worry love, just care for your children and remember I will always be there for you and if Jimmy gets violent with you again, you better come quickly to our shop and Dad will sort him out."

Christine embraced Ferzana and thanked her for coming to visit her in her time of need!

I was waiting patiently for Ferzana to come back to the shop to let me know what had been happening. When she told me the full story I was so disgusted. (I never told Christine or my family that Christine's husband had on many occasions asked me out for dinner!)

A few days later I was relaxing on my comfortable new chair just reading The Evening News, and then suddenly I heard a deafening painful scream, then loud banging noises,
   I swiftly threw my paper down and rushed out of the shop door.

The sight that I saw was awful. Christine had blood spurting everywhere (as though a butcher had been cutting at her) from her head and arms and she was in such a tormented distressed state. Christine painfully cried, "Jimmy is so drunk that he started beating me around the body and head with a long lead pipe. He just went berserk."

I ran back into the shop and shouted, "Dad, quick, Christine needs help." Dad rushed out from the back room and saw what had happened. I then quickly ran back to Christine (with my heart beating fast, at such a rate I felt it would explode). Rushing into the shop I quickly phoned the police and ambulance.

Sure enough, with sirens blazing, the first to arrive were the police, then the ambulance.
   Ferzana accompanied Christine into the ambulance, whilst at the same time trying to keep Christine calm. I cared for Christine's children, which, believe me, was a really hard job because they were so hyperactive and very upset at watching the terrible beatings their mother had to go through, but I did not mind caring for the children till Christine eventually returned.

Christine's husband had already ran away before the police came, but it did not take the police long to find Jimmy. Dad looked after the shop till Christine came back.

Christine finally came home and thanked us all so very much. If we had not intervened then Christine said she would have committed suicide, and as for her husband Jimmy, he was taken to court and charged with GBH. Jimmy's violence had finally come to an end.

After a week, Christine had made an appointment to see a solicitor and had started divorce proceedings. At least Christine and her children will not have to live in fear all their lives, I just pray that she gets over the awful trauma of her drunken violent husband.

My family and I will be keeping a close eye on Christine and her children to make sure that they are all safe. After all, what are friends for? A friend in need is a friend indeed.

Dad's last stern words on the subject were "If drunken Jimmy ever comes into this area he is a dead man. My big danda is waiting for him!"

August 23rd 1972

Dad's admirer

One of our regular customers is Mrs Shaw. She is a very-modern pensioner; she has beautiful large green beady eyes. She thinks she is sexiest woman alive. I would say considering her age she is an attractive lady. She has been widowed for just over four years now. Mrs Shaw lives with her chubby cat called Giggles that looks more like a fluffy baby bear.

Mrs Shaw is one of our regular and most devoted customers. She mostly buys honey, bread, milk, sugar, cheese slices and not forgetting her pet cat Giggles food called Yummy.

Mrs Shaw would frequently come into our shop at the usual time of six o'clock in the evening to buy her goods, as that was the time when Dad would be alone in the shop. Dad would be behind the counter serving other customers, but for some odd reason he always gave Mrs Shaw the goods that she bought at cost price. I wonder why?

Lately I noticed that Mrs Shaw had been continuously flirting with Dad. sometimes stroking his hands and then she would pout her lips, trying to get Dad overexcited, but then again, I put it down to my imagination working overtime, yet this seduction was getting out of control. Dad was enjoying this toying which she was starting to do regularly. Someone needed to tell Mum.

In the evening after our meal I asked Mum to come

into the living room as there was something important I had to tell her. Mum was confused and moaned, "What's the problem, Malika, you have been so irritable and moody for days. What's happened?"

I angrily said to Mum, "You know that dirty bitch, Mrs Shaw? Whenever she comes into the shop to buy her goods, she starts to seduce Dad. She looks into his eyes, whilst slowly wiggling her curvy body, and her low cleavage dress exposing the top of her breasts whilst flirting and touching dad's hand, it's probably all that honey she takes that turns her on. I feel like chopping her fat bloody wrinkled hands off." Mum was astonished and asked me to calm down as she would sort this dirty situation out.

The following evening at six o'clock Mum was waiting patiently for Mrs Shaw to enter the shop. Sure enough, she came into the shop wearing black, tight-fitting clothes. Upon her lips she wore the usual bright red lipstick, upon her eyes she had on her false eyelashes and she had very thick black eye make-up. She looked absolutely stunning. Dad served her with her regular goods, whilst her eyes kept looking left towards my mum. Dad asked Mum to make him some strong Punjabi milk tea (Punjabi tea takes a while to make) so I think Dad wanted Mum out of the way. As I quickly came into the shop Mum looked at me and winked. She asked me to make Dad's special Punjabi tea! Mum was adamant and stood her ground in the shop. Dad looked at Mum with anger in his eyes, then Mum politely and slyly said, "Oh, by the way your diabetic tablets are due and so are your high blood pressure tablets, plus don't forget your two manic depression tablets to cure your severe mental health problems, as if you don't take the depression tablets you can get very angry. You can take your medication with your Punjabi tea." Then Mum walked back into the kitchen with a cheeky grin on her face. Mrs Shaw's face dropped in shock. She was panicking, she would never have thought Dad suffered severe mental health problems. She quickly paid for her goods and did not wait for her change, she could not wait to get out of the shop. Dare I say it we never saw Mrs Shaw again. Good riddance to bad rubbish. As for Dad, he was flabbergasted as he never knew Mum had such a nasty streak in her, but now he knows he must never flirt back with the elderly widows, ha ha.

August 24th 1972

Mum visits her brother

Today is a bright sunny morning but for some reason Mum was feeling a bit depressed. She had tears flowing down her face whilst saying, "I am missing my brother Afzal who I have not seen for a long time, so I am going to visit him in London. That's if it is OK with you, Ali."

Dad calmly said, "My darling, you can go anytime! Get your suitcase packed and I will take you to the train station. If you wish you can take lazy Miriam with you, don't worry about us we are all right here."

Mum quickly went upstairs she took her small suitcase out from under the bed and packed the clothes she needed. Miriam also did some packing; she packed her large leather bag with clothes, sweets, chocolates and cake as well! What does that tell you about Miriam's weight, ugh!

The time now is eleven o'clock. Mum and Miriam were quickly ready. Dad smiled as he said, "Come on, let's get into the car and Malika, you start the engine."

Off we went to drop Mum off at the train station. Dad bought the tickets, then we all went in to give Mum and Miriam a kiss on the cheek. Mum and Miriam boarded the train and waved at us. My heart felt so very low as Mum and Miriam had never gone anywhere without us.

One day had passed then the following day into the shop walks Dad's cousin Auntie Zubida with her stepson Iqbal. I said, "Salaam Auntie and Iqbal" and they replied "Valakum Salaam".

Auntie and Iqbal walked quickly into the lounge and Auntie hugged Dad, asking how he was and why he did not go to London with his wife. Dad told Auntie that his wife felt depressed and low so she wanted to visit her brother.

I quickly made some tea and put some biscuits on a plate, plus some large creamy chocolates on another plate. I put the items upon a tray and left it on the coffee table. I went into the shop and sat in my usual place, suddenly I could hear whispering in the room. I quickly went to ear waggle near the lounge door and I heard Auntie whispering to Dad, "Don't worry, you say your wife has not contacted you yet, she should keep you up to date with what she is doing! If your wife and child do not come back I have a beautiful niece who is twenty-five years old. You can get married to her. Now don't worry, I am your cousin and I will be looking out for you."

Dad calmly said, "My wife and child should be coming back in a few days, after her little rest."

Auntie Zubida stayed for two hours, whilst still whispering to Dad to get married to her niece. What a cheeky bitch. Dad told Auntie he would be back in five minutes, he then walked to the chippy around the corner. Dad bought some fish and chips from the local chippy. The ugly bitch sorry, I mean Auntie Zubida, and Iqbal ate and took home a big box of chocolates from our shop. I did not even say goodbye to her or her stepson and they went on their way. Mum phoned Dad in the evening to tell him she was missing him and the rest of her children, and she wanted to come back that night. Dad booked her ticket to come back home. At ten o'clock that evening Dad and I went to pick up Mum and Miriam in the car. We parked up and walked into the train station. There to greet us was Mum and Miriam; they both hugged us and I cried, hugging Mum. We soon arrived back at the shop, I quickly made Mum a cup of tea, then I told her the news about Auntie Zubida and what she had said to Dad. Mum was upset and really shocked. In the morning Auntie Zubida phoned Mum to see how she was. Mum first spoke nicely then she said angrily, "I know what you had said to my husband. It is people like you who cause trouble in other people's marriages." Mum lost her temper and told Auntie Zubida not to come to the shop again. Well, goodbye to rubbish Auntie Zubida, the selfish, greedy bitch.

Auntie Zubida did not know the strong bond mum and dad shared, they love each other so much neither of them would ever be unfaithful. It's people like Auntie Zubida who cause trouble in people's marriages.

August 29th 1972

Hand in marriage

Me

Thursday early morning, and Dad's friend Uncle Yousef has come to visit Dad. Uncle Yousef has come to ask Dad for my hand in marriage for his nephew Jamal, who had conveniently arrived from Pakistan last week! Dad looked at me and I just put my head down (as that is what most young Muslim women do when someone comes to ask for their hand in marriage).

Uncle and Dad spoke amongst themselves and arranged a time for Jamal and his family to come to see me.

It was five o'clock in the evening and Mum had prepared such a lovely meal, consisting of meat biryani, chicken curry, pakoras kebabs and for dessert, sweet yellow rice. I quickly got myself ready. I wore my lovely shiny silk blue and white colourful salwar kamees and my make-up was immaculate, wow!

The guests arrived on time. I quickly hid in the kitchen whilst Dad asked me to bring the tea and biscuits in for our guests, which I willingly did. My hands were trembling as I held the tray which consisted of many goodies. I walked into the living room and left the tray on the old oak brown wooden table, whilst my eyes secretly looked up I could see a handsome, fair-skinned man with who, I presumed, was his father and there were two middle-aged women, plus Uncle Yousef. I then walked out elegantly and calmly. I was so excited.

Dad came out soon after me and asked me what I had thought of his prospective son-in-law Jamal. I serenely asked Dad, "If I stand at the top of the stairs, Dad, can you ask Uncle Yousef to bring Jamal out of the room and to walk him straight into the shop?"

Dad listened to me and he came out with Uncle Yousef and Jamal but I was completely and utterly shocked. What did I see? Were my eyes deceiving me? It was not the handsome man that I had saw, who was sat next to Uncle Yousef, instead it was the dark spotty skinned, chubby man who I thought was the handsome man's father. My heart suddenly sank as I whispered to Dad, "How could Uncle Yousef come for my hand in marriage for that thing? Get them out or I will start yelling."

I could not believe that they thought I would marry him. I am sorry to say the English temper had come out of me. When the guests and Uncle Yousef had left the shop they all had their despicable heads down in shame. I aggressively said, "Dad, you better fix that bloody illiterate Pakistani man. Why doesn't he get his daughter married to Jamal? Does he think I am a meal ticket to get his nephew residential stay in England?"

Dad had never seen my bad temper as he kept quiet and said gently, "Malika, you rest. You're not looking too well. I will look after the shop with Aftab."

It took a while for me to calm down, but from that day on Uncle Yousef had never stepped foot in our shop, and he had never phoned Dad since. Good riddance to bad rubbish. Yes, my temper has calmed down.

September 1st 1972

Uncle's frozen fish

Today Uncle Khan phoned Dad to say he would be visiting at about seven o'clock in the evening.

Uncle Khan is what you would call, tall, dark and handsome. He is about six foot three inches tall, has very dark skin, and beautiful mesmerising green eyes. His downfall would be his uncontrollable temper. He would always tell Dad his problems and complain about his wife Halima (who by the way, had not come to visit us, the reason being Uncle khan is always so rude to her in front of all of us). When we would tell Uncle not to verbally abuse her, he would shout "she is my wife and I can say what I like to the fat bitch" (definitely not a nice thing to say about one's wife). Uncle Khan does have a caring, warm sensitive heart, that's why I like him. It was his swearing I did not like. It is as if he does not show his sensitive side. Mum had already prepared the evening meal for Uncle Khan, his favourite hot chilli chicken korma curry and pilau rice, plus onion baji's and mint chutney, for dessert a scrumptious milk rice pudding; not forgetting his favourite Kashmiri milk tea.

Sure enough Uncle Khan came on the dot at seven o'clock. We all ate our well-deserved enjoyable, tasty evening meal, but I think I spoke too soon.

Uncle Khan called out to me. "Malika, come here for a second, give this expensive very tasty fish to your mum to cook. Tell her it is a present from me and can she please give me half the fish when it is cooked to take home for my lazy cow of a wife."

I looked inside his tatty old revolting, smelly red and white carrier bag and there inside was a very large, long fat silvery frozen fish, ugh! I quickly gave the fish to Mum to clean and cook.

Mum took one look as she held the smelly fish, and she moaned, "This fish is frozen solid. How on earth can I cut, never mind cook, this fish?"

I told Mum she was too fussy. I got hold of the fish, took it into the back yard and put a plastic sheet on the floor. The frozen fish was laid on top of the sheet, I got hold of a long very sharp knife and a small hammer. Over went the knife cut, cut, cut. The fish would not cut. Then on top of the knife I hit the hammer, bang, bang, bang. No way was that fish going to let me cut it. I laughingly called out to my uncle, "Uncle Khan, this fish won't let me cut it."

Uncle Khan came over to me and said, "Move away, just leave this awkward fish to the expert."

Well, Uncle tried to cut it, then banged it, and threw it. That darned fish would not let Uncle cut it. Uncle just went into the kitchen, leaving me alone with that darned fish.

By now all the neighbours cats were eagerly roaming around in my back yard waiting for me to get rid of the fish, so I wrapped that large frozen ugly fish into a black bin liner and threw it inside the broken brick garage. I then walked into the kitchen. I was cursing

Uncle Khan under my breath, "That silly old man."

Uncle was watching television whilst drinking a large mug of milky tea, with his large size feet upon the marble coffee table. He happily said, "It's so nice meeting up with my family after so long. Pity about the fish, please put it in the shop freezer and cook it another day."

Couldn't think, my Uncle Fishy, sorry I mean Uncle Khan, is such a messy person, with all his belongings scattered around the room and to top that he was giving us all headache with his problems. Before departing, Uncle would get a large carrier bag and put a potato bag, tins of tomatoes, bottles of orange juice and other groceries into it. He would wink and say, "Next time I come I will pay you for the groceries, bye bye."

With an uncle like him who needs enemies? From that day until now we all call him, Uncle Fishy the credit man (wonder why?).

September 5th 1972

Dad and the furniture

Today Dad phoned his younger sister Salmah. I like Auntie Salmah she is a sweet lady, and matching her personality she has a sweet tooth, poor thing, she only has a few teeth left in her mouth, hence why she is exceptionally overweight. she has thinning hair and is always giggling - Bless her.

Dad asked Auntie Salmah if she wanted a strong, brown good condition single wardrobe, plus two chairs and a few odds and ends. Auntie cheekily asked Dad if he could deliver the furniture to her house in Ardwick. Dad politely told her, "Don't worry, Salmah, I will definitely drop the furniture off at your house with Malika. We will be free on Monday."

Monday morning came and Dad was looking for the rope which he would use, to tie around furniture that had to be removed. Dad found the strong thick long rope and I helped him put the wardrobe on the top of the Cortina car (oh, how embarrassing). Next, he threw one end of the rope over the wardrobe, both ends of the rope were put through the windows and tied to the car doors. As for the chairs, they were squashed in the back of the car and believe me, at this time I was feeling very nervous, agitated and claustrophobic. There were lots of different sized plates, pots and pans which were put in the boot of the car, and I knew the pots etc. Would make a racket as I drive.

Dad exhaustedly said, "Right, Malika, are you ready? Now come on, let's get into the car."

Dad sat next to me in the passenger seat and held on to the rope ends for extra support. All I could think of was what must the neighbours be thinking?

My auntie was very mean with her money, she would always take and never give.

Why couldn't Auntie Salmah have hired a removal van? Just to save money she uses our car to deliver the free used furniture.

God forbid if we would have crashed it would have been the end of Dad and me.

Also I was terrified that the police would catch us, as Dad would have been heavily fined.

From that day onwards, Dad started to move furniture on a regular basis in and on top of our car. Sometimes I wished that Dad would get caught by the police and then he would not move furniture ever again in or on the car.

Luckily for Dad, he was never caught by the police.

September 12th 1972

Our black cat, Lucky

Our black male cat Lucky is such a friendly, cute cat. Lucky would sometimes hide in my bedroom away from Ferzana, the reason being she would shout at Lucky and then get the large brush to push Lucky out of doors. Ferzana thought that cats like to stay outdoors during the cold weather! Funny girl.

Our next-door neighbour Ben is very religious, he is a devout Catholic. He also has a black cat by the name of Billy. Now Billy is identical to Lucky, except for one whisker which was completely white.

One cold, dark evening I walked into the back yard to get the mop and bucket, but the sight which I saw upset me as well as shocked me. There was next door's black cat Billy – he was dead. His body was frozen stiff.

I tearfully ran to Ben's house, ringing his bell like a mad woman, whilst screaming out, "Quick, Ben, your cat Billy is dead in my back yard."

Ben looked curiously at me. He said, "Malika, my cat is behind me. That cat in your back yard must be Lucky." I was shocked, how could I have been so stupid?

I tearfully ran back to the shop. I told everyone that Lucky our dear cat had died. Mum took care of the shop whilst I put Lucky into a large strong blue carrier bag. How I wish we could have buried Lucky in our back yard, but we had no soil. In the morning, I reluctantly took Lucky to our vet, who then disposed of his body.

A few weeks had passed, we were all still distraught; it was like one member of our family had passed away. Aftab came home excitedly, holding a small cardboard box. He loudly called out to us all, "Malika, Ferzana, everyone please come into the shop quickly, look what I got from my friend Shahid's shop." Aftab knew we were all so upset about our cat Lucky dying that he went to the pet shop and bought us a cute black kitten.

We all pampered the kitten and took turns holding him Even Fezana was happy to see the kitten. What shall we call him? You guessed it! We called the little kitten Lucky! Welcome to the mad family, Lucky.

September 17th 1972

Dad's not well, plus I meet the love of my life

One bitterly ice-cold Sunday afternoon, Dad decided to keep me company in the shop. He bent down to pick up a large plastic bottle of orange juice which had unexpectedly fallen down from the above shelf, then without warning there came an unusual noise. You guessed it, Dad had accidentally ripped the left side of his trouser.

Two youths came into the shop. Dad knew them as they were brothers and their voices were loud, as they spoke with strong Scottish accents. One brother's name is Ian and the other brother is called John. They were in and out of prison for selling stolen goods. The brothers respected our family; they were polite considerate lads.

Dad looked at John and said, "When did you get out of prison?" Dad had been so upset on hearing about John going into prison. John was the one who supplied Dad with stolen goods.

John politely said, "Mr. Ali, you have a hole in the left side of your trouser."

Dad laughed for a few seconds then wittingly said, "Of course. Today I have a hole in my trouser as it is a holy day. It's Sunday." The lads laughed as they giggled ecstatically walking out of the shop.

Half an hour later, Dad was feeling a little unwell.

Normal people would rest when they have a bit of a cough and cold, but not my Dad. He loved to stand in the shop waiting for sympathy from the customers. Almost every customer would say, "Mr. Ali, you look very poorly today. Why don't you rest?"

Dad would say, "You know work has to go on, and you know I am not a lazy man." (Boring, heard it all before). Dad would not go into the back room of the shop for a break, he would rather stand there and get on my nerves moaning and groaning! I just ignored him and carried on reading my magazine. There was no sympathy from my side. Sure enough, Dad went into the back room of the shop for a well-earned rest.

Whilst Dad was resting, about one hour later into the shop walked this tall handsome Asian man. He smiled and said, "My name is Mohammed, how are you?"

I told him I was fine and we got talking about different subjects. Mohammed seemed really nice. I told him I had first seen him over a month ago at the doctor's surgery across the road. I felt this was truly the start of wonderful romance.

Under the guise of teaching Ferzana to drive, I had several secret dates with Mohammed whilst Ferzana secretly dated her boyfriend.

I couldn't help but feel smug as my whirlwind romance with Mohammed continued. Mohammed asked me to marry him. I asked Dad for his blessings but he refused.

Mohammed was more of a loner, seemingly he had no apparent income. The only income was what his rich parents sent to him from Pakistan.

Dad took a deep disliking to Mohammed. In a temper I left the shop and stayed at an old school friend's house for a few weeks and then I finally decided to marry Mohammed without my parents blessings. The marriage was not as wonderful as I had always thought it would be.

Neither of us had any means of income to support ourselves, so in the long-term we were unable to get a job. I was feeling so severely stressed, especially because of the terrible beatings Mohammed kept giving me. Eventually I decided to leave Mohammed.

Thank God, the marriage was not registered in this country, as it was only a nikah marriage. Eventually I had no choice but to return to my Dad's Prison Shop. Thank God, my family were still there for me. United we stand, divided we fall. Truly I love my family.

As for Mohammed, he is in the past, thank God. No one was to know about the nikah marriage.

September 22nd 1972

Mum the heroine of the day

Our washing machine had broken down and needed to be repaired. All the washing was piling up, so I decided to go to the launderette in Chorlton to get the clothes washed and dried. I thought I would be back within the hour, that is just before my moaning controlling Dad is due to wake up.

Mum, bless her, was in the back room, and my sister Ferzana said she would look after the shop until I got back, so everything was going as planned.

The clothes were quickly washed, dried and neatly folded back into the washing basket. Everything was finished, now time to get back to Dad's Prison Shop.

Upon entering the shop Ferzana, Mum and Miriam were so distressed. Mum shouted at me. I asked Ferzana what had happened. She cried, "A few minutes before you came back, two men came into the shop. One stood near the shop door and the other asked me for four packets of Park Drive cigarettes. I turned around to give him the packets of cigarettes, I then saw in his right hand he was holding a long sharp knife. He shouted at me to give him all the money from the till. I panicked and shouted for Mum, then Mum rushed out from the back room. She had a small knife in her hand because she had been cutting onions for the evening meal. She saw the youths and shouted at them. The youths panicked then ran off empty-handed, except for the packets of cigarettes in their hands."

I anxiously asked Ferzana whether Dad knew about the attempted robbery. Tearfully, she said, "This incident has just happened and I was going upstairs to tell Dad, but you came in." Thank God Ferzana did not wake Dad up from his sleep, if Dad knew that I was at the launderette at the time of the robbery, leaving my siblings alone in the shop, he would have gone berserk.

I nervously went upstairs and told Dad what had happened. I assumed the worse.

Dad panicked. He said, "Have you phoned the police?"

I said, "Yes, Dad, I have. The police are on the way."

But at that time I had not phoned the police, so I quickly ran downstairs and phoned them. The police eventually arrived and took statements from Mum, Ferzana and myself. The police asked about the description of the thieves, how old I thought they were, what colour skin they had, what clothes they wore and many more questions.

Later that day, we received a phone call from the police inspector, to let us know the thieves had been caught.

After a few days there was a court hearing and the two men were sentenced to time in prison.

What the thieves had not known was that Mum always took the notes out of the till every two hours and would only leave ten pounds in change in the till. What a wise and clever woman my mum is. She is our heroine, bless her.

September 30th 1972

Uncle Haroon came to visit

Mum's brother Haroon phoned to say he would be coming to visit us that afternoon, at about one o'clock. He lives in Leicester with his wife and two grown up children.

Uncle Haroon is an accountant and is very intelligent. He does not lose his temper and thank God, he does not swear. Truly, Uncle Haroon is the opposite of my dad.

This afternoon Dad was in a bit of a foul mood, the reason being our black kitten Lucky had done wee and poo in the corner of his bedroom. Dad went berserk. He got hold of the kitten and threw him out of the window on to the top of the shop's small roof, but the kitten jumped off the roof and landed safely on all four paws upon Uncle Haroon's shoulder. Uncle Haroon looked up in disgust and saw Dad staring back from the window with a guilty face.

Uncle Haroon said, "Ali, what nonsense is this?"

Dad apologised to Haroon. He said, "Sorry, Haroon, the bloody cat shit in the corner of my bedroom. I tried to grab him, but the bastard bit my hand."

Uncle Haroon walked into the shop, still a little shocked, and told Mum what had happened. Uncle Haroon said, "Sister, you better keep an eye on Ali, I think he has some sort of behavioural problems or he could be having a nervous breakdown."

Uncle Haroon soon relaxed when he smelt the sweet aroma of the delicious meal Mum had cooked for him: meat and spinach curry, meat samosas, potato cutlets and for dessert, Uncle Haroon liked simple jelly and custard.

Uncle Haroon had a large bag with him which he quickly opened. Inside the bag he took out a present for Mum – her favourite perfume, Opium – and for the rest of the family a large tin of chocolate biscuits, plus some Asian sweet Mithai which was made in Leicester.

Uncle Haroon stayed with us for five wonderful hours, he would talk about the past and how naughty he was when he was a teenager. He was a gangster but he soon changed his nasty ways, that's why he went to live far away in Leicester to get away from the bad company that he had hung around with in Manchester.

I think Uncle Haroon had enough of Dad's antics and was worried what Dad would do next. He was happy that he did not live in Manchester, he would go insane with Dad's unusual habits. Well, no one can change Dad; we all love him the way he is and would not change him for the world.

October 2nd 1972

Grandma's visit

Hurray! Grandma is coming to visit us today. Grandma is not the fragile type, she is very hyperactive and sometimes a very rude elderly lady.

Grandma's hair is grey with a touch of orange henna, she always keeps her hair neatly tied back in a tight smart bun, she loves wearing makeup – her face powder was so light that her face looked like a ghost, and her lipstick was blood red, ugh. Grandma is coming all the way from London (escorted by her plump son and obese daughter-in-law). Uncle Abdul and Auntie Zara, between them must weigh at least fifty stones, and I am not exaggerating! Uncle Abdul is always out of breath, mostly due to his overweight problem. He has a long moustache, which gets in the way when he eats his food (how disgusting, especially if you have to sit next to him at the dinner table). He also stutters and we have to finish his sentence for him, but despite his faults he is a generous man.

Auntie Zara has long black silky hair with a few grey hairs popping up here and there. When she walks she bounces towards her left then to her right, she also has a faint, thin moustache which is very distinctive. Her hands are huge, and her height must be at least six foot. If I had not known her I would have thought she was a transsexual.

Grandma last visited about six months ago and she

stayed with us for two weeks (seemed like a lifetime). Only joking. One thing which was worrying me about Grandma was her unusual behaviour, her rudeness and her swearing, when she started she could not stop! Grandma could not care less who was listening; if Grandma didn't like you, she would let you know instantly I wondered whether these were early signs of dementia.

Whilst peeping out of the shop window, I saw Uncle's battered red Cortina car parking up. Yes, Grandma and the rest of the family had finally arrived.

Their meal was already prepared, just the way grandma liked it, which was boiled rice, hot spicy meat curry, cauliflower curry, lentil curry and onion bajees, with yogurt plus salad and for dessert, Grandma's favourite sweet dish, halwa and sweet yellow rice. Grandma had a dirty habit of sucking the meat off the bone, whilst unaware of the dreadful sucking noise she was making (how revolting).

Directly after dinner, Grandma would fiddle in her handbag and take out her sweet tasty paan (a green beetle leaf consisting of sugar fennel seeds and tobacco). Grandma would never offer her paan to any members of the family.

All the family gathered in the warm clean lounge. Grandma had a routine of sitting comfortably on the black leather sofa with her legs resting on the coffee table. She also had a disgusting habit of letting of gas in front of all the family and friends, pew! She even had a small metal spitting bowl near her to spit the pan juice out, ugh.

Grandma has such disgusting habits, but we all love her, God bless her.

Grandma then pointed her finger towards Uncle Abdul and beckoned him to go and bring her black bulging leather suitcase into the lounge.

Uncle Abdul placed the heavy suitcase upon the coffee table, and one by one grandma handed everyone their presents.

Grandma loved to buy us all different coloured salwar kameez, the traditional Pakistani clothes, plus matching glass bangles, matching slippers and golden shoes. My mother was regularly given tins of halwa which were bought from Karachi, and believe me, Grandma bought five small tins of halwa to keep Mother happy.

In the evening, Grandma would be sat on Dad's comfortable rocking chair and talk about the past. Nobody wanted to listen to her except me. Grandma would laugh and cry at the same time, remembering incidents from the past; some were happy, some were sad. She remembered the time she had tenants living in her small terraced house in Manchester. The tenants were of Irish descent, the husband was light-skinned with rosy red cheeks, but had a violent nature, he was small and fat and he had a large mole on the left side of his face. His wife looked fragile. She would wear long black skirts and matching cardigans; she was tall and had short dark hair,

Grandma remembered when her son (meaning my dad) went to the pub to socialise. Sometimes she had no choice but to send a family member down to the pub to fetch my dad back home, because the tenant was physically abusing his wife.

Grandma said, "The tenant soon calmed down when he saw your dad. The tenant knew he would beat him black and blue then your dad would ask questions later."

Grandma used the nasty swear words once again, her famous swear words were, 'Yeh kutta hai' and 'Woh kutee hai' (in other words, 'he is a dog' and 'she is a bitch'). She would talk about the large scar on the top of her arm (Grandma told my mum a lie) that many years ago, as a young adolescent, she accidentally fell and her glass bangle cut into her arm. Now, after so many long years, Grandma told us the truth, that when she was twelve years old she was very protective of her friends. One day she tried to protect a friend and she fought with a Pathan girl (Pathans are known for their bad temper and aggressive behaviour whilst fighting). Grandma was arguing with this Pathan girl, suddenly the girl put her hand down her brassiere and took out a flick knife. She opened the knife and cut my grandma on top of her arm, then she ran away. Grandma ran home and her mother took her to the hospital (my God, the mischief my grandma used to get up to when she was young).

Grandma was like a tape recorder, she would not and could not stop talking. On a few occasions her false teeth fell out, but we all loved her all the same. Besides having slight hearing problems, Grandma had cataract in her eyes. Poor Grandma's legs were now going bow and she needed an operation. Grandma was too frightened to have an operation. She had a bad habit of repeating questions, one being where her son Abdul was (Abdul is my mum's younger brother). Grandma slept in my bed and believe me when she snored nobody in the house could get any sleep. Did I get any sleep? You guessed it, no.

Grandma liked to go to the cash and carry with me and Dad. We had to pull two shopping trolleys: one for the stock, the other lower trolley for Grandma to sit on. She would sit with her legs on the trolley, while holding her handbag and large red and white shopping bag. I would love to see what she had in her red and white shopping bag.

I would happily push her around (I think she enjoyed the ride).

Grandma was going back to London and, as usual, she would always put a twenty-pound note in each grandchild's hand, then they were given such a sloppy kiss on their cheeks (ugh! Only joking). Bless her, I love her very much.

Grandma phoned to let us know they had all arrived safely back in London and that she would be coming back within three months (just can't wait, ha ha).

October 6th 1972

Mary lost her baby

Mary, who is a tenant in next door's house and a very good friend of mine, is five months pregnant. Mary asked me if I could accompany her to St. Mary's Hospital, the reason being her recent blood tests showed some abnormalities. I spoke to Dad and he said, "You can go, but due to my diabetes please try to come back early as I am tired and need my sleep." I told Dad that I would try my utmost to come back quickly. Mary came back into the shop, I collected my car keys and off we went to the hospital.

Waiting in the waiting room we both felt very tense, especially when one does not know the end result. Then a nurse appeared, calling for a Miss Mary Shaw. We were escorted into the doctor's room. The doctor had much sadness on his face and sadly said, "Miss Shaw, I am sorry to say it is not good news. On your stomach scan and important blood tests, your baby has many deformities, plus brain damage and a hole in its heart. The chances of your baby's survival are slim to nil, and if he were to be born he would probably only survive a few hours. You have an option to give birth or terminate the pregnancy."

Mary cried hysterically, fearing what she had felt in her heart. She knew she had no choice but to terminate her pregnancy. Mary looked at the doctor and miserably said, "Doctor, I have no choice but to have a termination. If you can tell me which day and what time I will come to terminate my much-wanted child."

The doctor said, "Mary, the next available

appointment we have is in a few days time on Thursday at nine o'clock in the morning."

Mary thanked the doctor for all his kind help and advice he had given her. She put her head down, with her heart slowly but surely breaking. I told Mary to please be strong and not to worry, I would accompany her on the termination day.

Thursday rapidly came around, and as promised I took Mary in my car to the hospital for her termination. A room had been prepared for Mary; she had been given a tablet, now all we could do was to wait. I waited nervously outside the room praying with all my heart that all would be over quickly, and Mary's baby would swiftly be born. Sobs were heard from the delivery room. I then quickly entered her gloomy room and consoled Mary as she looked at her lifeless little baby boy. Mary had to stay in hospital whist the priest came to pray on her baby and arranged a funeral for her baby. I kissed Mary on the cheek and told her I would always be there for her. When Mary came out of the hospital the funeral arrangements had already been finalised. Mary named her baby John; unhappily, Mary said the funeral would be the following Monday. Monday soon arrived. Dad shut the shop so we could all go to the funeral, so sad such a wanted child. I felt compelled to write a poem about Mary's baby.

October 7th 1972

I was compelled to write a special poem

A POEM DEDICATED TO MARY AND HER BABY

WANT TO LIVE, BUT BORN TO BE BURIED

Want to live but not meant to live
Floating within this purified water
Of my mother's loving womb
Head above and sometimes below
Unborn within this hidden tomb,
That I call my home
My mother carries me with the utmost care
My mother is still unsure if I will be born alive
Yet! I am sure I will not survive
This illness will not allow me to thrive
This womb, this everlasting tomb
Will be the last place where I will breathe
Where my heart will gradually stop beating
Where my movements will finally end
As yet! My eyes have not seen any life
Only my own miserable passing life
This bubble in which I live,
And will soon be departed from
I will enter the living, but death itself had come calling
No fault of mine. No fault of my mother's
I am a much-wanted child
Yet I am ill and so premature
Small drops of tears trickle down my face
The time is close, it's very near yet I have no fear
My heartbeat has slowed down, it has now ceased

No breath, no movement, no tears
Now I just wait in this death tomb
Just waiting to enter the world of the living
There will be pain for my mother and all the others
But for me I await to be buried once again

October 15th 1972

Ferzana took me shopping

Ferzana was in such a cheerful mood she said, "Malika, come on, get ready and we will both go to town in the car."

Ferzana said she wanted to take me shopping to buy me some new clothes. I thought how unusual and how kind, she is for thinking about me for a change.

Dad said he would look after the shop, and lovingly said, "You sisters enjoy yourselves but you must take Miriam with you as she never goes anywhere. Do be careful she does not get lost and you must be back within three hours as you know it is my sleeping time. Also, here is ten pounds for you both to spend there." I thought how unusual, he must want a nice peaceful time with Mum!

Ferzana sat us in the car and raced of towards town. Sure enough, she kept her word, Ferzana treated us to a lovely warm meal of fish and chips, plus peas and two tins of Coke, yummy. After a heavy meal, Ferzana said, "Come on, now let's do some walking. Oh, and by the way, I have an appointment to get my hair cut so I should be about an hour. Here is ten pounds, go and buy yourselves something. See you both in an hour," then off she went to get her hair cut.

I held Miriam's hand whilst we crossed the road to the Marks and Spencer store, then we went to Lewis's. It was surprising how long ten pounds lasted us.

There were many offers on in town. I bought myself two long dresses, one black, the other red. Miriam bought a talking doll and a pink and white dress, and then off we went to look for Ferzana.

One hour and twenty minutes had gradually past, then at last Ferzana was in sight, but not by herself. She was walking hand in hand with a young handsome tall Asian man. Ferzana saw us and beckoned her friend to go and whispered something to him, then the man went rushing off! Well, Ferzana, you're at it again, using us as bait to see this man. She never learns.

Ferzana begged us not to tell Dad and that she would buy us an expensive ice cream and chocolates. Well, bribery sometimes does work, ha.

Nearly three hours in town and we were getting tired, so thankfully we headed home.
Dad would be waiting for us outside the shop.

Upon arrival Dad asked us if we enjoyed ourselves. Ferzana said with a smirk to Dad, "We certainly did enjoy ourselves," then she winked at me and Miriam.
Now back to the shop and behind the counter once again, whilst Dad takes his well-earned rest.

October 20th 1972

Zarina and her daughter

Such a miserable day, it's raining buckets. Mum's friend Zarina is coming with her unruly sixteen-year-old teenage daughter Shamma. It's now two o'clock in the afternoon and sure enough in walks jolly chubby Auntie Zarina with her teenage rebel daughter Shamma. Auntie smiled then with a loud echoing voice said, "Asalaam Walukum, how are you? I pray you are well and happy, my dear."

I happily said, "I am very well thank you, Auntie."

Shamma looked at me up and down and nodded. Truly she looks as if she has an attitude problem. I told them both to go into the lounge as Mum is expecting them both.

A few minutes later I could hear Auntie complaining to Mum about her daughter. I popped my head into the room for a quick nosey. I saw tears flooding down auntie's face and she angrily said "you don't know what I have to go through with Shamma, she is very rude, she swears at me, and answers me back. I have been widowed five years, I miss my darling husband so much, Shamma has changed for the worse since her father's death" My mum was absolutely shocked at what she heard from Zarina.

Shamma looked very angry at her mother whilst raising her eyebrows and furiously shouting, "Stop acting like a drama queen, Mum. I help you clean around the house, what more do you bloody want from me? You only give me ten pounds for helping you! Truly you piss me off with your bloody acting. Dad used to hit you, I don't hit you, do I?"

Mum looked at her friend Zarina and felt so sorry for her, especially hearing from her daughter's mouth about Zarina being physically abused by her deceased husband. Now it looks like Shamma is taking over the nasty role from her late father.

Dad just happened to be listening outside the lounge door. He had his danda in his right hand, then Dad opened the door slowly and peeped into the room. He frowned, looking at Shamma, whilst shaking his danda. He looked towards Auntie Zarina with a painful smile.

"Asalaam Walakum, sister Zarina. How are you? Just got my danda. I thought there was a trouble maker in the shop." Dad looked irritably again at Shamma. "You know, Sister, if you have any problems at all with anyone, even a relative, I will quickly come to your aid and even to your home with my ferocious danda and smash their bastard shitty arses with my danda." Dad then looked at Shamma again, who by this time was shaking and frightened. She knew that Dad was talking about her.

Auntie Zarina smiled as she said, "Brother, I know you are all here for me in my happiness and sadness. I appreciate all that you do for me, thank you." Mum had prepared a lovely meal consisting of lamb curry, roast tandoori chicken portions, pilau rice, and for dessert homemade rice pudding.

Excitedly, Mum said, "Right, come on, let's all go into the kitchen and have our well-deserved meal."

Shamma kept peeping over at Dad and his dangerous danda. She was petrified as she saw the nasty, rude bad-tempered side of him.

After all this commotion, Shamma had changed her bad attitude problem; she was so pleasant to everyone. Dad told Auntie that he will come on Tuesday to repair her broken door. Mum and Auntie hugged each other, smiled and waved goodbye.

Dad kept his promise and arrived at Auntie Zarina's house to do her door repair. Shamma sat silently on the sofa. She dare not say a word, but managed to say Salaam. Auntie Zarina told Dad how grateful she was. She smiled and humbly said, "I cannot believe how Shammas bad attitude has changed to good. She is more loving towards me. Thank you so much, brother. May God always keep you and your family happy Ameen."

Well! Dad, your famous danda worked it's wonder once again.

October 26th 1972

Dad is still unwell

The cold, foggy weather has arrived once again, making us all feel shivery and a bit moody. When the weather is warm Dad seems to get headaches and bad temper rages.

Dad had recently been feeling unwell – tired, hot, dizzy and thirsty.

In the morning at nine o'clock, Mum phoned Dr Harris's surgery for an urgent appointment for Dad. The receptionist told Mum to send Mr Ali into the surgery at ten thirty a.m. this morning.

Dad arrived at the doctor's surgery at ten o'clock in the morning. The doctor did a routine check-up and got the nurse to take some blood samples from Dad. The nurse said, "Mr Ali, we will get the blood test results in a few days."

A few days later Dad's blood results came through. Dr Harris wanted Dad to make an appointment to see her. All the family were so worried, what had the blood test results shown?

Dad's doctor appointment date soon arrived, I accompanied Dad into the doctor's room. The doctor told dad that the blood results confirmed that he has high blood pressure, high cholesterol, abnormal liver results, and to top all those he also showed signs of having gallstones, and that this is the reason we have to now have heart x-rays and some other essential scans to confirm any other illnesses.

Meanwhile the doctor gave dad a prescription, a long list of medicines were prescribed.

Dad was shocked to hear all these ailments he had.

All the family felt so sorry for Dad, so he was fussed on and given some much needed pampering.

Mum made sure that Dad had no sugar in his tea, as a replacement she used sweeteners. Sweets and all sugary puddings were stopped. Dad has a bad, ferocious temper, we will always love him but; sometimes you have to be cruel to be kind! But we dare not tell Dad that all sweet stuff is banned for him, because he may decide to show us his famous danda.

November 5th 1972

Fireworks

Bonfire night is upon us once again (that means fireworks) with a capital B for bang. Dad sold fireworks and believe it or not, he had a license to sell fireworks! Dad had bought bangers, rockets, rainbows; such an assortment of fireworks to sell in the shop.

Today is November 5th and the fireworks are selling like hot cakes. The time now is seven o'clock in the evening. I can smell the smoke from the bonfires and I can see the fireworks as they explode, such wonderful colours into the darkness of the night.

A little while later in walks a boy aged about sixteen; wearing a black and white scarf, wrapped around his nose and mouth, he had a hood over his head and was casually looking at all the expensive fireworks. I thought this doesn't look too good. I slowly pressed the bell which rang into the living room and Dad rushed out. The lad saw Dad and walked out of the shop. A couple of minutes later that same lad rushed into the shop and tried to steal forty pounds worth of fireworks. Dad stood in his way and grabbed his hand, then within a second, his friends who were waiting outside lit a firework and threw it into the shop. Dad had to let go of the thief's hand. Whilst the other thief threw the chocolate stand on the floor, Dad quickly threw a cloth over the firework which had already caused a lot of damage. There was smoke everywhere, there was damage to the counter and other boxes in the shop.

Aftab ran after the thieves with a stick, but soon came back. Dad also tried to run after the thieves, but I stood adamantly at the shop door. Ferzana got hold of Dad's legs and told him that the thief and his accomplices might have a knife and might stab him. We told dad it was not worth running after them they may have other weapons (meaning guns). I told Aftab he was stupid running after the gang.

Dad phoned the police, meanwhile we were all badly shaken over this horrific incident. It was as if everything had frozen in time and then played back in slow motion. The police soon came and asked for a description of the lad, all we could say was what we saw, which was not much. He was of a slim build and around five foot and nine inches tall and of mixed race, not much to go on really! Especially that his face and hair was covered with his hood and scarf.

After we had all recovered from the shock, we all helped in the cleaning of the shop. Dad vowed never to sell fireworks again – he was not prepared to put his family at risk. At least we can now go to the fireworks displays around our area, well that's fantastic. It will be a night out from the Prison Shop.

November 10th 1972

Poems became my life and soul
Poems make my world whole

The crying garden

Nothing stirred but tears
Naked tree branches frozen in time
Naked except for the mouldy leaves that remained
The long green blades of grass overbalanced
Paralysed as if in death of a winter's night
Flowers remained adamant
As if forbidden to dance
A portrait, a picture card
A sense of loneliness

Nothing stirred; nothing heard
No birds chirping, no bees buzzing
But wait! There is a sudden movement
Three squirrels, two squirrels then one squirrel
Disappearing down cracked flower pots
hungry bleeding claws scratching fanatically
To gain their well-earned prize

Now darkness descends
The curtain must come down slowly
That is until the sun rises
The eyes will once again see the portrait
of the crying garden

November 16th 1972

When I get a moment I reminisce and reflect and let my pen take over, I just love writing poems.

The cold wind

The cold breath of icy wind
as it splashes over my eyes
Freezes my nose
Sores my mouth
the breath like death itself
Drilling painfully into my skin
dampening my bones
the splinters within the wind
Sent from the devil himself

DEMISE

The moon has broken it's silver mirror
The sun has terminated its warmth
The clouds paralysed with disbelief
The blackness of the night awaits
The earth is deep in siesta, death has crept within life
The victim lay pale and motionless
The angel of death has conquered

Grown old

I have grown old, please be kind and speak calmly to me
All I wish from you, is for you to listen to me
All I wish from you, is to be patient with me
All those embarrassing mishaps please don't yell at me
When I am unable to feed myself please help me
When you were a child I lovingly washed you,
I lovingly cared and fed you
When you cried I hugged and comforted you
Yet now I am feeble and unable to take care of myself
My eyes blinded through crying blood tears
Thinking constantly "Will you", "won't you"
Or are you governed by inheritance and greed
Please my child will you take care of me in my hour of
need

November 27th 1972

Dad took us all to Blackpool

Dad got up very early today (how unusual). He said, "Come on, we will all get ready and go to Blackpool. It's such a warm lovely day today, we will enjoy ourselves. We deserve a rest sometimes!"

Mum was in the kitchen excitedly making pakoras, kebabs and cheese sandwiches, she also packed four large bottles of cold drink. Mum packed all the food in a small suitcase, then made a flask of tea, got a kitchen roll and pushed it into the little brown suitcase.

Within one hour everyone and everything was ready. We just prayed Dad did not change his mind and cancel the trip.

Whilst waiting in the sitting room I could hear a car horn, first once then three times. I ran into the shop and looked out of the large shop window. I saw a black van outside and inside the van sat chubby Uncle Rehman. I shouted to Dad, "Come quick, Uncle Rehman has come. He is waiting outside." Dad was humming as he opened the shop door, and eagerly waved as he said, "Coming now, relax we are all coming out now." Dad called for everyone to come outside and sit in the van, Dad closed the shop and put the shutters down. Everyone happily sat inside the van; we could not believe Dad had actually arranged an outing to take us all out to Blackpool. Whilst we were all in the van we sang Cliff Richard songs, one being, "Summer holiday" and many more holiday songs.

Upon reaching Blackpool, Uncle Rehman parked his van in the car park whilst Dad gave Mum twenty pounds to spend on the family. Dad and Uncle had to see a man about some business. Before going Dad told us to go on the rides and then eat something and to enjoy ourselves – they would be back in a couple of hours.

Mum took us all towards the exciting fast rides, The Big Dipper and others. Later we had some of Mum's delicious food she had lovingly prepared, along with some chip shop food, chips and cheese pie, yummy. Lovely. Our tummies were absolutely full, besides Miriam being sick, all went well. Then we went towards the beach for half an hour; we walked towards the sea, throwing pebbles for luck. Miriam built a small sandcastle, it was a bit wobbly but it looked cute.

Time had quickly passed. Dad was busy looking for us, he found us kicking a ball about on the sand. Dad told us to clean up and meet him in the car park and we would then be on our way home.

Once at the car park, Uncle Rehman and Dad were each holding three black bin liners which were bulging! We wondered what was inside the black bags. Dad said, "There were lots of Asian clothes going cheap–" (in other words, probably stolen) "–so I thought I would buy some clothes to sell in the shop, very cheap yes! Very cheap."

Well, at least Dad took us all out for the day, even though it was for his gain. Now we were back on our way to Ali's Shop, Dad said strictly, "When we get back, open the shop for three hours, then we will close the shop." We all put on a miserable face not wanting to talk to Dad, then suddenly Dad said, "Only joking, I wanted to get you all agitated, ha ha." Dad could have fooled us, ha ha. Bless him.

December 4th 1972

Dad's at it again

Such a lovely warm sunny afternoon, just wishing I could go out for a walk but there was no way dad would let me go out as he was expecting a couple of business friends (thieves). The men had promised Dad that they would be bringing some Christmas decorations, plus chocolates, Christmas cards and much more, Well, here we go again.. Dad never stops buying stolen goods. What can I say? That's my dad for you.

Two hours had passed, and then suddenly two scruffy, bearded Asian men came cautiously into the shop. One of the men said in a husky voice, "Can we speak to the owner of the shop, as he knows we are coming. We have the goods he ordered off us."
     My heart was pounding thinking, are they about to rob me? As they both looked a bit distrustful, I told the men I would call my dad, so I took a large breath and shouted at the top of my voice, "Dad, can you come into the shop, two men want to speak to you."

Dad came rushing into the shop with his famous danda in his right hand, but when he saw the two men he had a happy money-making smile upon his face. Dad told me politely to go into the sitting room whilst he talked business.

Half an hour later, Dad and the two men fetched lots of large and small parcels into the kitchen! I went into the kitchen to have a nosy, Dad said with a sly grin,

"We are going to make lots of money from what is inside these parcels, so let us start opening them."

There was parcel after parcel and it took us a while to open them all. It was all Christmas stock, decorations, cards, chocolate boxes, Christmas bulbs and lights, ladies and men's gloves, false jewellery, small beautiful Christmas trees, and so much more. All I was thinking was, Oh my God, not again, Dad. He should have learnt his lesson from the last time when he got caught with stolen goods. As they say 'a leopard never changes it's spots, he never learns, well that's extra work for the rest of our family.

I truly could not believe it, just a few hours later our customers were pouring in, they were quickly buying the cheap Christmas decorations and all the other goods Dad had bought.

What can I say? As Dad's saying goes, 'money has to be made, by hook or by crook'. That's my Dad for you. He will never learn.

December 17th 1972

Ferzana's work Christmas party

Ferzana worked part-time at the local Karmen chemist. She was excited – the reason being her manager had arranged a Christmas dinner for all the staff.

The venue is at The Domino Club which also has a restaurant. The restaurant is located in the town centre. Ferzana told Dad about the Christmas dinner and that everything had been paid for by her gay manager Dan. The staff had to meet on the 22nd December, at seven o'clock in Manchester town centre, near the bus station then together everyone will walk down to The Domino Club.

Ferzana nervously asked Dad if she could go to the venue after work. Dad grunted then crossly said, "Definitely not. No daughter of mine is going to a club, even if it has a restaurant."

Ferzana cried. I told her not to worry as on the day of the Christmas dinner I would call a taxi which would take her to The Domino Club.

Ferzana wittingly smiled and said, "Thanks sis, much appreciated."

Today is the 22nd December and it's Ferzana's Christmas dinner party. We prayed that everything goes to plan.

Ferzana is wearing a beautiful low-cut black and

silver glittery outfit, black leather shiny high heel shoes, diamante earrings and matching necklace, dazzling silver hat, black gloves and silver bag. The jewellery makes her look wealthy and elegant. She looks beautiful, so stunning, elegant and dashing. Wow.

I phoned for a black cab taxi in advance, booking it for six thirty. The taxi arrived on time, and I whispered to Ferzana, "Hurry up! The taxi is waiting outside."

Ferzana quickly stepped into the taxi and was driven to her destination, phew! We were so happy that Dad unknowingly slept on.

One and a half hours later Dad had awoken from his catnap. He asked Mum, "Where is Ferzana?" Everyone kept silent. Dad knew Ferzana must have disobeyed him.

Dad shouted, "Malika, get in the car and start the engine, whilst I tell Aftab to accompany us."

Mum and I nervously wept. I said, "Dad, leave it, let her enjoy her Christmas dinner with her colleagues." Dad told us to shut up and sit in the car. We had never seen Dad so upset. Dad could not understand why Ferzana had defied him.

The roads were so busy because of the rush of the Christmas parties. We had reached our destination as there in front of us was The Domino Club. I parked the car as near as possible, whilst Dad and Aftab entered the restaurant, looking for Ferzana. Dad asked the lady at the desk if a call could be made in the restaurant area for a Miss Ferzana to come to the reception area. A few minutes later Ferzana arrived. Dad and Aftab came out with an entirely embarrassed Ferzana as Dad bellowed at her.

I sadly said, "Sorry, Ferzana, it was not my fault Dad woke up early, instead of the usual three-hour sleep."

Ferzana despondently said, "I was about to have the starters of my Christmas dinner and then Dad spoke to reception to call out my name Oh, it was so embarrassing." Ferzana then calmed down.

We all knew Ferzana was more petrified of her father's temper than of missing her Christmas dinner. Ferzana recognised it was better keeping silent than having her arms and legs broken with Dad's famous danda.

December 25th 1972

Christmas

Christmas time is upon us once again, and almost every one of our customers wished us Merry Christmas and a Happy New Year. (Dad would even leave a little bowl full of sweets for our customers to help themselves; as it is Christmas.)

On Christmas Eve, the male customers would come into the shop as drunk as lords.

That's the time Dad seemed to stay longer in the shop!

Many male customers wanted to give us sisters a kiss on the lips for Christmas and another kiss for the New Year, some of the men even bought their own mistletoe.

It was stressful telling the male customers it was against our faith to kiss men with the exception of our husbands. Gradually the men understood that we are Muslim women who are not allowed to kiss men except their partners. Our customers respected our wishes, it was either respect us or have the wrath of my dad upon their heads! In other words, they would get the big danda stick upon their drunken heads. (Just like our old milkman John).

There was only one reason I felt so upset on Christmas Day, the reason being my dad would make us open up our shop, and it was so embarrassing. We all wanted to sit and relax and eat our Christmas dinner, and watch our Christmas programmes. Dad was adamant that he wanted the shop open (what a mean man; no rest even on Christmas Day).

Living on the premises above the shop was difficult. Nobody had the courage to say to Dad, please close the shop, it's Christmas Day. I used to hide at the back of the shop up until the shop got busy then I would come and help serve the customers. Many customers still came into our shop when they should have been resting. They would buy chocolates, cards, biscuits and non-alcoholic drinks.

The best thing we would look forward to on Christmas Day was the Christmas dinner, (which, by the way I had to cook). Secondly were the presents, which my siblings always bought for the family on Christmas Day. As they say, no rest for the wicked Still, what could we say to Dad, he was the boss and he had to be obeyed.

Roll on Boxing Day!

January 1973

A year has passed

Now, my dear friend my diary,
you know my inner secrets
Days have passed, months have passed
Now a year has passed
All this year had been pleasurable
But a little hectic
I knew I could not change the past
Perhaps the future can be changed
I had also enrolled at college
The truth being just got a bit bored
I never knew it; till I tried it
I became a published poet
I became an author and an artist
I wrote one poem
Then ten, then a hundred, then thousands of poems
Many poems were published in books
Many published in magazines
I had found my true love of life
Which was reading and writing poetry
I had written
"Life goes on, even after we are gone"
Roll on the New Year.

Ali's Prison Shop

Ali's Prison Shop is the diary of a young woman named Malika who is faced with the difficult decision of deciding where her cultural loyalties lie. Malika considers herself entirely English and thinks her parents Asian culture is old-fashioned and restrictive. She and her siblings (two sisters and a brother) are the only Asian children in their school and they live in a wholly English area in Manchester in the early 1970s. This diary is mostly based around true happenings. Ups and downs, some funny some serious. Malika's father, Mr Ali buys a small convenience store which quickly becomes his pride and joy. At first, Malika thinks of the shop as a novelty and enjoys the passing custom, however, she slowly grows to resent the shop, she feels as though it's more of a prison. Malika decides to get married, to escape the pressures of life in her Dads shop.

Diary of Ali's Prison Shop

Diary of Ali's Prison Shop